Cousin

Henry Potter

and the

TERRIBLE

Time

Machine

by Henry Potter

AT Publications
P. O. Box 68
Thompsonville, IL 62890

Chapter One

"The Shadow"

Maybe he saw a ghost - I don't know. My limo driver was so nervous, he slammed the car door, and flung gravel all over my leg as he screeched onto the pavement.

Those eyes! Why did he refuse to even drive me onto the school grounds? I stood there shaking my head - watching him burn up the road.

A dazzling flash flicked in the distance like a dragon tongue. The sky's getting dark. "I don't care," I thought. Just think where I'm going!" I kicked a rock as I turned to walk down the winding lane leading up to the secret back entrance of the school for wizards.

Hi, I'm Henry Potter. I live a long way from here, but I got a tip as to where my cousin Harry is, and came looking for him. I finally got him on the phone; otherwise, I'd never have known about the back way in. He was excited. Me too.

Soon after his parents were murdered, my father moved us far away. He was afraid we'd all be killed. Dad never mentioned his dead sister's family. Harry and I were just babies. I didn't even know he existed until a few weeks ago. I couldn't believe it!

You can guess what was running through the limo driver's head as he burnt rubber, but I had no clue as to what Harry and I were in for.

There it is. I see the gate. Kids are in the yard doing something. Just before going through the entrance, a shadow passed over the grass in front of me. What was that, an airplane? It happened so fast - I didn't know what hit me. I was knocked out.

"Are you alright?" someone said. Things were a bit hazy as I looked up at a bunch of faces.

"How did I get down here? Who are you?"

It seemed like I was in a dream as I heard cousin Harry's voice. {Actually, it was a dream. I didn't know it, but they carried me into a little yellow cottage and put me on a bed. Before waking up, I would experience unearthly things.}

"It was that old wind-bag wizard giving you a warning," Harry said. "He knows that you're coming to see me. Don't worry, I can handle him. Just stay close to me and you won't have a thing to worry about. If you come to this school, you'll learn how to take care of him yourself."

"Yeah!" everyone shouted.

It was great to finally see each other. How would you have felt? After they all greeted me, Harry showed me around the campus.

Summer vacation was just around the corner, and final exams were coming up, but we really wanted to spend a little time together. We stood on the grass chatting excitedly.

"Let's take a walk." I said. "Is that alright?"

"Yea let's do it. You can meet more of my friends later."

The sky kept getting darker. We ignored it. Down the shady, wooded lane we went - {the same spooky looking one I had just been on} - talking about what had happened to us since that awful day when his parents tragically died. Thunder rumbled in the distance.

Suddenly Harry stopped, "I've just got to study," he said with a determined look as he threw a rock at a tree. He bit his lip. "Well, I guess it won't hurt to go a little farther. We won't be long will we?"

"Not long."

"We're coming to this crossroad," Harry said. "Which way ya wanta go?"

"Let's go left."

He was so full of questions. Both of us were.

"Sometimes I've wondered," Harry said softly. "Don't get me wrong. It isn't that I don't have great friends here. I love them. It's just that - for so long, I didn't think that I had any more blood family. Are you a wizard?"

We walked on for a while, forgetting what time it

was, and before we knew it, we found ourselves gazing at the entrance of what Harry said was an enchanted forest.

"Cool!" I croaked.

A big sign standing there listed cautions about certain things in the forest that might be hazardous to your health.

We could see gorgeous, rare flowers that Harry said were poisonous to the touch. Some kind of a giant animal was waddling down the path. A funny ducked-billed hopping creature was in the distance. Off yonder we could see a flying octopus land in a flowering Eggyoke tree.

"What is this - an enchanted zoo?" I laughed. "Let's go in!"

"I don't know about that" Harry warned. "I've always been cautious about going into this place without my broom."

"You been in here much?"

"Sure!" One cool thing about this forest is that things in here are symbolic.

"What do you mean?" I asked.

"Hold on, you'll see. One of the most dangerous things in here is that you never know when one of those flying octopuses might attack you, and try to have you for dinner. And there are other enemies that are even worse.

"Can we go in just a little way?" I begged. "I want to smell one of those weird-looking flowers over there. How did this place get here anyway?" I could see that Harry was thinking hard.

"Well," he said, "maybe if we don't go in far, and don't stay long. But don't forget, I've got to study!"

"OK! We'll be back before you can count to - - What is that!"

My eyeballs must have been big. There was a giant slimy anteater. We ran past it.

The farther we went into the forest, the darker it got. "This is a creepy place," I squawked as we walked fast.

As we slowed, I asked, "Are there any good things in here?"

6

"Oh yes," he smiled. "There's the village of little puppy people. They love to come up and jump all around you. It makes you feel right at home. Then there is the town where the gentle blue giant people live. They have kind, friendly eyes, but don't say a word. There are tigers with no teeth, and there's that miserable wizard who lurks around in here trying to do all the damage he can. He's the one who gave you the warning as you were coming in to see me. We really shouldn't be in this place. We've gotta get out of here soon, and I think you can guess why. When we're on my turf it's different, but now we're on his turf."

"Ok. We'll go soon."

"But beside all that," Harry said, "this forest is the home of the wise and wonderful professor Tuliphead."

"Professor Tuliphead! Who's that? And why would he want to live in here?"

"He's a really interesting scientist who's working on a secret project that very few people know about. He's been a consultant for the government space program, and has worked for years on an amazing machine. His new Trilla-septigahertz computer system with three hundred fifty seven trillion-septillion gigs of

RAM has helped him perfect it. I accidently stumbled upon his place when I was exploring. He and his wife are very kind to me. But I can't tell you about his project unless you promise to keep it a strict secret.

"Alright" I said.

"You promise?"

"Yes."

"You sure you promise?"

"I'm sure" I said, raising my hand.

"Alright. There's no better place than this forest to work on such a project. Most people are too scared to even come into this creepy place. Even the guys on the four-wheelers and the BMXs stay out - especially since one of them got eaten by a flying octopus."

"If a flying octopus catches you, what does it do?" I said.

"Oh not much. It just sucks the juices out of you and uses your bones and hair to enlarge its nest." Harry's face was twisted up.

My brain was tweaked. "Tell me about that machine you mentioned. But first, tell me how the professor lives in here with that freaky wizard. Why doesn't the evil fiend hurt him, or drive him crazy?"

"Oh, they have a certain understanding to leave each other alone," Harry said. "I don't understand it all, but the professor is smart, and I think that he has just out-foxed the old wind-bag."

"How is that?" I said.

"Well, the wizard knows that if he bothers the professor, he can get hurt in certain ways. So they just stay away from each other. I'll have to ask him more about that when I see him next time.

"Concerning the machine, the only thing I can tell you is what I wrote on these paper napkins here in my wallet."

He took out some scrunched-up napkins, and started reading.

"Here it says, 'It works on warp atomic digital linear-wave power, and is so powerful that . . .'"

"Wait a minute! What did you say?"

9

"I said 'warp atomic digital linear-wave power.' The professor said that this thing is so powerful that it can turn mass into energy, and energy back into mass."

"Whoa. Turning mass into energy is what an atomic reaction does."

"That's right! But here's the rest of it. It says this machine is able to harness frequencies of energy from extra-galactic space. Then by concentrating, modulating, and focusing them into the nuclear linear-wave transformer, it is able to intercept and capture the very frequencies which went out into space from events of the past.'"

"That's the most ridiculous thing I've ever heard."

"I know, but just hold on and listen to the rest of it. It says, 'When these frequencies are then focused by nuclear neutrino lazar concentration technology into the materialization monitoring chamber, the professor has been able to tune in both people, and events that existed long ago.'"

"I don't know about this man," I said. "Has he been in a nursing home?"

"Absolutely!" Harry stuck out his tongue at me.

"Listen now," he barked. "It says, 'By harnessing what scientists call the 'great power' {which holds atomic particles together}, the 'little power' {which causes them to pull apart}, along with gravity, and electromagnetic energy, the machine is able to turn the mass of whatever he puts into the chamber into pure energy. Then it straightens the wave form into nearly a straight line, and projects it into space much faster than the speed of light. Then, by re-modulating it again into frequency form, he is able to bring it back into the machine - - and under nuclear pressure, the machine is able to re-form the matter back into the materialization chamber.'"

"Whew! Do you understand all that?" I said.

"No way," Harry laughed. "That's just what I have on this napkin. But that's not all. What I just told you is what the machine could do four months ago. On this other napkin it says 'By using sub-atomic, inter-nuclear methods, Professor T is able to project the mass of objects, animals, or people into the near future."

"Have you seen this thing? Have you seen it

11

work?" I said.

"Yes, I've seen it. And no, I haven't seen it work. When I was at his place last, he was feverishly working on it - trying to perfect it by the first of this month."

The two cousins had gotten so caught up in what they were talking about that they didn't notice the giant flying octopus swooping down upon them.

"Look out!" Harry yelled - pushing me to the ground - as the octopus whizzed by - waving its tentacles to catch a fresh meal.

"That was close. Let's get out of here! I recognize where we are. Unless we take shelter, that creature is coming back," Harry shouted. "You don't want your juices sucked out of you do you?"

"Not today."

Harry puffed - "I know that the professor's house isn't far from here. Let's stay behind this giant tree until that thing goes away, and then we can go to his place for a while."

"OK," I said, breathing hard. I could see the octopus rising higher. It's giant wings flapping, and its tentacles waving wildly as it started to turn around to come back for another try.

"Why won't it just come down here on the ground and chase us down?" I gasped.

"They have to catch their prey while flying. They're so slow and clumsy on the ground that anyone can get away from them. Let's just leave it alone, and get out of here. I want to see the professor as much as you do."

From behind the large tree, we saw the creature fly past us above the path, and then swoop up over the trees. It was gone.

We were silent.

"It's clear. Let's go," Harry said softly.

We were wide awake now - going as fast as we dared while watching above our heads in all directions. In a few minutes, we came up - panting - to the entrance of the professor's gorgeous home.

Inside the gate, we passed lush, green grass. Beautiful flowers lined his walk. Neatly trimmed shrubs stood just below the large picture window of his living room. An earthworm wiggled on the sidewalk.

"What a relief to be in a safe and pretty place like this," I thought.

We didn't notice the professor's guard tiger lifting his lip into a growl - revealing its toothless gums. But before either of us could see it starting to crouch into a pounce position, we heard the professor's kind voice - "Cume een, cume een!" he said.

Professor Tuliphead, coming out onto the porch to greet us, knew exactly what was happening.

"Now dear Fangface," he said, "vwhat do you tink you're doing? Dees ees my friend Harry und hees companion. You mustn't stalk dem - you hear?"

The professor sent Fangface back to his mat where he lay down to keep watch.

"This is my cousin Henry Potter," said Harry. He's visiting, and, it's a long story, but we ran here because a giant flying octopus almost got him for his next meal."

"Oh dat vwould have beeen terreeble," the professor said.

"I saw him coming, and knocked Henry down just

in time. Florida has its alligators. We have these monsters. But now that we're here, I wanted to see you could fill me in a little more on that new machine you've been working on. How's it coming along?"

"Oh, eet's cuming along better dan I had expected," said the professor. "Een fact, I'm about vready to send my vreport to dee scienteefic community so dat eet can be published een dee scienteefic yurnal.

"Did you get the machine to do all that you were trying to get it to do?" Harry asked.

"Ya my boy! I have fine-tuned und perfected dee process of ultra atomic vworp-vwave focus so dat not only have I beeen peecking up people und events of dee past, but vweeth dee techniques I've perfected, I am now able to proyect matter boote eento dee past und eento dee future.

"You'd better not let certain people get a hold of that thing," I said. "Men with warped brains could really mess up a lot of people with it."

The professor continued - "Yus yesterday, I proyected a rabbit eento dee past, und put eet eento dee bedvroom of dee palace of dee turd dynasty of dee pharaoh of Egypt. Do you vrealize vwhat dees discovery science und to dee vworld? But vwe must ful veeth eet, for to power deese machine eet tomic energy - which ees dee most powerful produced on dee eart."

"If it's so powerful, and dangerous, how are you able to do these things here in your laboratory" I asked.

"Oh my boys," the professor's face became serious, "you see, dough dee nuclear vreactions are very powerful, dey are done een a small area, und are very concentrated. Dee vorp-atomic vreactors are far under dee ground."

"So there's no noise?" Harry asked.

A smile came on the professor's wrinkled face. "Not much. Dee reactors are encased een lead, steel, breeck, sand, und cement, 90 feet theek."

"That's great," Harry said, "but are you sure that this machine really works?

"Ya my boy. Eet vworks perfectly. But I cannot take dee credit for all dee vresearch dat vwent eento eet. My friend und colleague Doctor Veenie Von Bun has helped me tremendously. Und also de famous Doctor Nikovnikov has done a lot of vwork on it. I

16

could not have done eet vwithout deez men. Vwe have proven to my scienteefic sateesfaction dat eet vworks all dee time, und can be regulated to proyect matter bote eento dee past und eento dee future."

"How far into the future, or into the past will it send things?" I asked.

"My expereements so far have taken living animals as far back as about tirti five hundred B.C., und, as far forward as two vweeks. As you might expect, going eento dee future ees far more deefficult, und eet takes a deefferent technology. But I'm vworking on sending tings farder eento dee future soon. At dee same time, eef I ever proyected matter too far back, eet might become detransfixed from dee specified atomic vorp-vave frequency, und I might loose eet.

"You mean it might be locked onto that frequency, and be trapped in the past forever?" Harry asked.

"No. Eef an obyect goes too far back eento dee past, dee modified frequency vwould become so vweak dat dee machine could not extrapolate eet back vweeth vorp-vwave nuclear suction eento dee present. But eef I am careful not to send dee object farder back dan tirdy five hundred B.C. dee machine vworks perfectly!"

17

"You've proven it?" I said.

"Ya."

Now I was really curious. "But how did you know that the rabbit you sent into the past really went there, since the animal can't talk to you?"

"Dat's a good qvestion my boy. I know dat eet actually vwent eento dee past - to dee place vwhere I sent eet, und came back because of two tings. Number voon, vwhen I put dee animal eento dee chamber, calibrated dee instruments for dee time; dee coordinates of dee location, und pushed dee buttons, detonating dee computer vregulated nuclear vworp vreactions, dee animal deesappeared, und vwhen I opened dee chamber door, eet vwas gone.

"Did you see it disappear?" I asked.

"Ya!" His eye seemed to twinkle as he said, "Dee atoms of eet's body turned eento energy, und I saw eet vanish.

"Secondly, vwhen I closed dee door, und at dee proper time, vreversed dee vreaction, dee animal appeared on my screen een dee chamber, vright on time, und vwhen I opened dee door eet came out unharmed een

18

any vway."

"But wait a minute," I said. "It's true that you saw it disappear and re-appear, but how do you know that it went to Egypt, to the place where you wanted it to go? Did you see the Egyptians? Did you see the Pharaoh on your screen?"

"Ya," the professor said with a big smile. "I could see a very leemited view of de vroom dat eet vwas een. I saw dee Pharaoh und hees attendants. Dey looked surprised to see Shurlock, und got all excited. Dey vran avround, to get some kind of a vweapon to keel heem und have heem for deener, but before dey could hurt Shurlock, I brought heem back here. Den dee poor Egyptians vwere running avround loooking for heem. De Pharaoh got mad und - I couldn't understand vwhat he vas saying, but eet loooked like he was going to trow hees attendants een jail."

"You called his name Shurlock" Harry said. Where is he now?"

"Oh, hees een dat cage ober der. You can pet heem. He's a gentle ting."

"You know," Harry said, "I was wondering if

19

you could do me a favor."

"Ya?"

Just then, we heard the back door open. Someone came in. The professor went into the kitchen, and we heard him say, "Cume een Darling."

It was Lilly.

"Who's here," I heard her say. "Is it Harry Spicer?" She was trying to whisper.

"Ya, you got eet." the professor said. Eet's Harry und hees cousin Henry."

Lilly had on a lovely red dress. Her sandy-brown hair just touched her shoulders, and was livened up with a white ribbon, which was tied into a pretty bow. She seemed like a kind and gentle person. Her eyes beamed as she came in to get acquainted, telling us of the adventures of the day.

Though Lilly was a bit younger than the professor, they were happily married. Their place was neat and restful, but there was no way that she could know the horrors that were about to happen in their quiet home.

After talking a bit, Lilly brought us all a cup of herb tea. "I grow these herbs right here in our yard," she said. "This tea is my favorite."

It was really good. "It tastes like a blend of peppermint and roses," I said.

"You like it?"

"Yea, I really do," Harry said.

"Me too"

"Now den, vwhere vwere vwe? Ah ya," the professor said to Harry, "you vwere going to ask of me a favor."

"Yes sir. I've been wanting to know what some things in the past were like. What my parents were like before I was born? They were murdered you know."

"Ya, I. . . . I'm very sorry," the professor said sadly.

"I would love to see and hear them before I was born. It would comfort me very much if I could go back - just for a little while - to see and hear them."

"Vwell," said the professor, "I'll have to tink about dat."

"You said that you perfected the techniques didn't you?"

"Oh ya!"

"Then there's no problem - - right? My broom won't take me back there."

"Vwell, vwe must be super careful," said the professor. "Eef anyting happened to you, I vwould be held responsible."

"I know," Harry said. "But I know that you're a trustworthy scientist. If you say that you've already done this procedure accurately with both objects and animals, then I trust you to do it for me. Do you have any doubts about the machine professor?"

Harry's words were positive - hitting him between the eyes.

"Do you know for sure," Harry said, "that it has worked, and that it will work again and again, and that it will work for me?"

The professor didn't hesitate this time.

"Ya!"

"Then when can we do it? Is the machine ready now. Can we do it now?"

Harry had forgotten all about studying for his exams. He would remember soon.

"Eet might seem like a coincidence," the professor said, "but vwhen you boys came eento my yard, I vwas getting vready to send an animal eento dee past und place eet een a certain location at a certain time."

Then Harry said, "How long will this take? I've got to go soon and study for my final exams."

"Oh, eet vwon't take long," the Professor said. "You see, you can be sent back a tousand years eento dee past, und see events vwhich seem to take a long time, und yet, be brought back eento de materialization chamber vwitheen about 20 meenutes."

"Well," Harry beamed, "if that's the case, then let's go! But I have one more question. After you send me back a ways to see my parents, can you then send me into the future only one week so that I can see what grades I'll get on my final exams? That would be great! Is that too much to ask?"

"Vwell, eef I carefully calibrate dee instruments, dee computerized nuclear vreactors, etc., I tink maybe vwee could do dat. But don't ask to go any farder forvard dan dat! Not now."

"O.K!"

"Yus tree vweeks ago, I have already proyected an animal a vweek eento de future to a certain location in Portsmit. Den, after a vwhile, I brought eet back. After a vweek vwent by, I checked veeth dee people at dat location, und sure enough, dee animal had beeen der vright on time. Vwhat I'm saying ees dat eef you vreally vwant to do deese vweeth all of your heart, den I am vweelling. You vweell be dee first human. So eet vweel certainly prove to dee scientific community dat my machine vweel vwork eef I have living proof of eet in dee form of a boy. I vwasn't meaning to make you into a pig from guinea ."

"Oh no, Professor," Harry said. "I don't feel like a guinea pig. I feel honored to be the first person in the world to be able to do this.

"Just think Henry, I'll be able to see my parents while they were alive and young!"

"Professor Tuliphead," I said, "I also have a favor to ask."

Looking kindly at me he said, "Vwhat ees eet my son."

"Can I go with him? How can I sit here and watch my cousin go off into the wild blue yonder, and not go with him? This is the most important and historic moment since Columbus discovered America. This place, these people, this event, will go down in history as the beginning of a new age for the entire world! You'll be famous, and so will we. Is there room in that chamber for both of us?"

"I tink so," the professor said. "But you bote vweell have to be vary careful. Yus seet ober der for a leetle vwhile as I prepare dee instruments, und it vwon't be long unteel I'll be vready. Vwould you boys like some more tea?

"Darling, vweell you bring de boys more tea

vwhile dey're vwaiting. Be sure you bote use de vrestvroom before you get eento de chamber."

I could hardly believe what was happening, or what was about to happen. I was too excited to talk, and just stood there staring out the window.

Suddenly, a shadow passed across the grass in the front yard. What was that? An airplane?

Chapter Two

"The Trip"

"O.K. boys," the professor said. "Dee instruments, dee computers, dee vreactor, und everyting ees vready!"

Harry and I walked over to the materialization chamber like we were in a dream. We carefully, slowly, stepped in, and sat on the bench-like seat. It was hard and cold. I looked at Harry. His face was cringing.

"Are you boys alvright?" the professor said.

"It's a little cramped, but we're fine" I said." "How about you Harry?"

"I'm alright. I'm so excited, I wouldn't care if I had to sit on your lap. I'm feel great."

"Alvright boys, I'm going to slowly count down from ten. Vwhen I get to tree, take a deep bret und hold eet. Seet very steel und don't move. OK? Here vwee go.

"Ten. . . Niner. . . Eight . . . Seven . . . Seex. . . .

We didn't dream that we would never see the professor again.

Five . . . Four . . . Tree . . ."

I took a deep breath. @#$%^#%$@#$%*#(@!^) !%^#%@#$%!*^#(^*!%^#%$@#$%^^&#$%##%$ Black. Black. Black. Black. Roaring - - Squealing - - Whitish - - - - Black - Where was Harry? - "Where are my parents?"

I squinted my eyes. It was so dark and hazy. I could barely see his face. It was all screwed up.

"Where are we?"

28

What happened to the boys? What happened to Harry's parents? They never saw them. The cousins would learn later that the shadow Henry saw going across the grass in the front yard was the old wizard who wanted to kill the boys for coming into "his" forest.

While the boys are in the materialization chamber and the nuclear reaction is just beginning to start, this "mad man" comes crashing through the professor's front window, and pushes him up against the wall amid the screams of poor Lilly.

The fiend then takes a huge club and smashes the lever of the warp-wave nuclear reactor. He rips the lever all the way out, and throws it across the room - #%*#&%*@&%#!.

The professor's eyes show the horror he feels. He struggles up off the floor, trying to stop the fiend, but it's no use. Again the dark demon shoves the poor man against the wall, and down to the floor.

Wheeling around, he pushes Lilly with a great thrust over a chair.

Down she goes.

With a terrible grin, the wizard leaps onto the professor's chest, stands there for a moment in triumph - while Lilly screams, and without a word, the crook hops onto his broom, and shoots through the window into the sky.

The ground is shaking. A rumbling - like dull thunder is heard under ground as the warp-wave nuclear reaction is going wild. There is a great puff of smoke in the materialization chamber. The boys have disappeared. They keep going and going - back, back, back, at warp-speed - two, three, four thousand, five thousand, six thousand years - - back, back . . .

"Aaaaayyyyeeeeeeee!"

A few seconds - and they're out of the Milky Way. They've zipped 50 million light years into space, past the large "Virgo" group of 2000 galaxies - each with 200 billion stars.

On the warp-wave linear frequency, they're accelerating - - billions of times faster than the speed of light.

They're a billion light years from earth. 5 billion. 10 billion. The boys look around. Their mouths are open. In shock, they look at each other.

They're still sitting next to each other, but the materialization chamber is gone. They look back. Before their astonished eyes, they have a glimpse of the large scale universe - - galactic clusters, flaming nebulas, constellations, blazing super novas and systems - converge in front of their dazzled eyes like shining chains and threads of a glowing, lacy curtain.

Out, out, they race until the eerie cosmic curtain of light is covering the infinitude of darkness before them. They have a feeling of stark nakedness and smallness before the vastness that surrounds them. In minutes, they've gone 46 billion light years from the earth - - and they've only just begun.

Their hearts are trembling and shaking

- - for from the black and terrible depths of the cosmos - the "warp turbo effect" takes place, and now they wheel away into endless space.

Sometimes with solemn flight of angel wing they flee through zaarahs of darkness, through wildernesses of death that divide the worlds of life. Then from a distance that's measured only by infinity, light dawns upon them through a sleepy film. By inexpressible pace the light sweeps to them. By unspeakable pace they sweep to the light. In a moment the rushing of planets is upon them. Then the blazing of suns is around them. On the right hand and on the left tower mighty constellations that seem ghostly from infinitude. Past number are the glimmering archways and gates.

Henry: "I'm scaaaaaaaarrrrrrrrred."

Through the middle of a galaxy they flash, hardly seeing it - not knowing that they are still accelerating, and are going 261 trillion times the speed of light.

Looming before their astonished, atomized brains are immense stairs that scale eternities below. Above is below, and below is above as they flash past blazing systems unnumbered, and the hearts of the boys sink - - and - - stripped of gravitating bodies they cry out

"End is there none to the universe of God?"

Suddenly a shining being is beside them with words of courage. Then on again they fly at warp speed - until systems behind them are out of sight, and specks of light before them are transformed - as blazing nebulas approach and flash above them, and pillars of immensities, and architectures of galaxies unspeakable in dimensions pass beside them - and their hearts sink again - as they cry out -

"End is there none to the universe of God?"

And chains and fiery sheets of blazing galactic wheels and infinities echo the question with amazement -

"End is there none to the universe of God?"

And this echo finds no answer. And the boys streak past immensities, and eternities, until suddenly - as myriads of swirling galactic wheels sweep past them – a mighty cry arises – that systems more mysterious, that nebulas more billowy, that heights and depths, are coming - are at hand – and the cousins shudder and weep - and Henry cries out, "Angel - or whoever you are -- we can go no farther! Our spirit aches with this infinity. Let us lie down and die - for we are overwhelmed with the pain of this vastness - for there is no end."

"End is there none?" the being solemnly demands. Is this the sorrow that kills you?"

But there is no voice to answer.

Then the shining being throws up his glittering hands to the heaven of heavens, saying "End there is none to the universe of God. Lo, and there is no beginning."

At this, the mysterious being intercepts their terrific, blinding pace, and slows them.

The messenger has given the boys time to

34

get used to his brightness - and now he comes closer. They at last find speech.

Harry: Who are you? How do you know us?

Camero: I've seen you both out here from the time you started. You are trapped. I know all that has happened, and unless someone helps you, you are doomed in this time - space warp forever.

Henry: Are you a ghost?

Camero: No.

Henry: Are you a dead person from the earth?

Camero: No. The dead are dead. They know nothing. I am alive. I am one of the messengers which the Great King created for his pleasure.

Harry: Where do you live? Are there many of you around? What's your name?"

Camero: You may call me Camero. It means "Friend." There are billions of us, and it's our job to bring messages to the many planets from the Great King.

He made them all.

Harry: The "Great King?" I never heard of him. Where does he live?

Camero: He lives at the center of the universe. He is very kind. We messengers are older than the earth that you came from. The Great King made us before he made your planet.

Harry: How come we never see you guys on earth?

Camero: You do. You just don't know it most of the time.

Henry: Are you sent to earth by the Great King?

Camero: Yes. Most of the time we are invisible, but sometimes we disguise ourselves as one of you. Many times we have saved the lives of many of you earthlings without you knowing it. Many of you have talked with us, and haven't known who we are. But that doesn't matter. As long as our mission to help you is accomplished, that's all we care about.

Harry: If the Great King is kind - as you say,

then why are things messed up on the earth? Why is there death and suffering, and pain?

Camero: You are going to learn the answer to that question. But first, you must learn some other things. I have interrupted your journey. We are sitting relatively still here in a quiet spot in the universe so we can talk. But you are about to see something that earthlings have hardly dreamed of. You are about to see the home of the Great King. When I said that we are sitting relatively still, I mean that I have stopped your terrific speed, and we are now going slower than the speed of light. But we are moving, and are orbiting the city. Everything in the universe orbits the city of the Great King.

Harry: Everything?

Camero: Everything.

Henry: I can't believe this is happening. Is this for real? Harry, are you alright?

Harry: I'm alright. I can't believe this either. Camero, will you please show us what you are going to show us, and then, I want to go home. I want to go back to earth where we came from. Are you able to help us get back there? By the way, you don't know how grateful we are to you for coming to help us. Without you, we would've just kept going on for ever. I thought we were just going to go back in time about 15 or 20 years to see my parents who were murdered. Why are we out here? You said that you know what happened. Will you please tell us?

Camero tells the boys what the wicked wizard did to the poor professor, to the machine, and to Lilly.

Camero: All of your questions will be answered. In earth time, the professor has been working hard and struggling to fix and calibrate his machine, to bring you both back. But you have been sent back in time so far that the earth does not yet exist.

Harry: Oh dear! I can't believe this! You mean we're living and talking to you right now before the world began?

Camero: That's right.

Henry: I don't understand that.

Camero: You are going to go back to the future earth. But on your way, you will be like a "read only" file in one of your twenty first century computers. You will not affect, or be affected by anything you are about to see.

Henry: I've never been so shocked in my life! I still can't believe this is happening!

Harry: I feel sorry for the poor professor. Oh, I guess he doesn't exist yet either. But if the world doesn't exist yet, how is the professor going to get us back to a world that doesn't exist? It's kind of confusing.

Henry: We're the ones out of sync, not him. He stayed right where we left him. We're the ones who don't exist - not on earth anyway. I wish we could get out of here and go back to earth right now – but since it doesn't exist yet, I guess we're going to have to wait for Camero to help us.

Camero, are you going to directly send us back home, or are you going to let Professor Tuliphead bring us back with his terrible time machine?

Camero: I'm going to have to send you back to the time on earth that you came from. Even after the earth comes into existence and is thousands of years old, and the professor is born and gets old enough to make his machine, he will never be able to get you both back to where you came from. He will fix his machine, but when he tries to bring you boys back into the materialization chamber, it won't work because he will not be able to calibrate the machine to the exact worp wave frequency that you were sent out on. When the machine was damaged, the record of that exact frequency was corrupted, and the professor will never find it.

Don't worry. I'll make sure that you get to earth in the 21st century. And yes, your request to see things in the future will be granted also. You will see much more than you even asked for.

Harry: Cool! But are we going to have to wait thousands of years for the world and the professor to exist before we can get back to where we left him?

Camero: I know that it's hard for you to understand, but as Henry just said, the professor is exactly where you left him. He didn't change - you did! You are the ones who have gone back in time so far that the earth doesn't exist. You're going to have to be patient and let me help you get back to the future. Just relax. I'll help you.

Harry: Thanks Camero. That helped a lot. I was starting to panic. But where is the first place we'll go? We're still out here in the middle of no-where. What is the first thing we'll see?

Camero: We are going to the city of the Great King. I will now enable you to fly along with me. Stay close to me. Here we go.

Chapter Three

"The Tour"

The boys with their guide, now change directions, and again travel at warp-speed - - in, in, to the very center - to the very heart of the great and endless universe itself. Past galaxies, constellations, fiery suns, systems without number they fly. Their eyes are wide as they pass - great sheets of shining cosmic dust hundreds of light years across.

Henry: I see an intense light looming up in the distance. What is that? It's taking the shape of a gigantic city sitting on top of a rainbow! Look at that Harry - it's so bright! Look at those colors! I've never seen anything like this. What are those colors called?

Camero: No language of the your future earth will have names for them. At the time that you came from earth, no humans had ever yet seen such colors with their natural eyes. They do not exist there.

Fifty million miles outside the city walls - in all directions - is the sterilized "Vacuum" where no matter exists. At the edge of the "Vacuum," the three stop. Here, Camero fills the cousins in on what to expect in the city and how to act.

Soon, the three start streaking inward through the 50 million miles of "Vacuum" toward the dazzling city. The travelers appear like flashes of lightning. They will arrive at one of the twelve gigantic gates in a little over four minutes. As they approach the "City of the Great King," the eyes of the two are gaping. To their amazement, the vast city looks like a glowing, rainbow-tinted orb in space with numberless, shining messengers moving in and out of the light.

As the three move closer to the city, Henry can't stop his thoughts from bursting out of his mouth.

Henry: It's huge! It's vast!

Camero: Here we come. Stay close behind me now as we approach the sentinel at the gate. I must present to him the golden card.

After presenting the golden card to the tall, gleaming guard at the gate, their messenger leads the boys in through the gate into the city.

Once inside, they stand on lush, green grass, looking around. Camero gives them time to adjust to the intense brightness of the place before going further. The boys stand silent.

Harry: How do you feel Henry? I'm trembling.

Henry: I can't describe it. I've been blown away. Just look at that - - - - and that. Look at that! This must be the most gorgeous place in the universe. Look at those walls! I can see right through them! I'm starting to get used to the light. It makes the colors of the trees, grass, and flowers so bright! I've never seen such fantastic things in my life Harry! I smell the flowers over there - a little like orange-blossoms and roses.

Harry: What could those walls be made of? Look at those buildings Henry! They're magnificent.

Henry: Massive! - - - Beautiful! I never knew such things could exist. This place is fit for a king.

Camero: A King indeed. This is the home of the Great King. He made it. It is a fitting place for the one who made the galaxies, the planets, and will soon make the earth.

Henry: Make the earth! Oh that's right - I forgot. It doesn't exist yet. Are we going to see the earth being made?

Camero: You are.

Harry: This is unbelievable! I don't want to be disrespectful, but I'm a little curious. I was wondering how He made this place. Did he have workers do it for him? If so, where did they get the materials to build it - you know - out here in the middle of space? And where would the workers come from in the first place? And where did they get the beautiful animals, and the seeds for the flowers and trees?

Camero: The Great King made it all just like he made everything else - including me. He spoke, and it was.

Harry: That was it?

Camero: That was it.

Henry: Awesome! We're just at the entrance of this city. We haven't hardly seen anything yet, but I can tell that this place is so vast and majestic that I feel unworthy to even be here.

Camero: Indeed. The radiation here is so great that if your human body from earth were brought into this city in its natural state, you would cease to exist. The nuclear radiation and light here is even greater than that which occurs in the center of your sun. You are standing in more radiation than if you stood inside of the greatest nuclear explosion that earth scientists could ever produce. But the ethereal body which you now have is able to endure it.

Henry: Can we go through walls like Superman, and swim under water to see the fish without having to breath? And can we walk around on the sun, or inside of it, and not get burned?

Camero: Yes.

Harry: Cool.

Camero: But you are going to see that as you take your journey back to the future - - back to the earth when you left it, those are not the kinds of things you are going to be thinking about. You boys are going to see the future with its agonies, and with its ecstasies. The time is coming when you will have a part to play in helping people to determine their own futures for life or death.

Harry: I don't understand that.

Camero: I knew that you wouldn't. But you will understand my words more as events unfold before you.

Harry: Henry and I have so many questions!

Camero: On your way back to earth, you'll learn many things, and your questions will be answered. You'll understand why you exist, and where you are headed.

But come. I will begin now to show you some of the beauties of this place. Follow me on this golden path, and I'll take you on a tour of the city.

Henry: I kinda like this place. Who could want anything more gorgeous! I'm finally starting to relax.

Camero: As we walk away from the gate we just entered, coming up on our right is a field full of all kinds of flowers. This may have been some of the delectable fragrance that you were smelling as you came in. There are millions of exquisite flowers scattered all over the city. The Great King loves flowers. He loves beauty, and in this city are thousands of varieties, which are so elegant, that no one could ever improve upon them. You'll smell titillating fragrances from scintillating flowers which no one except those in the city have ever seen or smelled. In the city you'll see things of supreme loveliness which you have never seen. These flowers will never fade. Like the city itself, they are eternal. Over there on the left, we see a field of tall grass.

Harry: Man! That's the most beautiful grass I've ever seen. It's living green. Look at it Henry. It sparkles with silver and gold!

Camero: The next field we're coming to is filled with all kinds of animals. Over there you see lions, leopards, and wolves - interspersed with many sheep and lambs. Do you notice that they are all together in peace?

Harry: Whoever heard of such a thing!

Henry: They're following us. They must be intelligent. It just dawned on me that since the earth doesn't exist yet, these same animals that we are familiar with on the future earth, were in this city before they were on the earth.

Harry: That brings something else to my mind. I used to think that all of these animals, as well as the rest of us - evolved over millions of years from worms and germs. Now I know better. How stupid I was to think that such lovely and beautiful creatures just accidently developed with no one's mind and heart to plan what they would be like.

Camero: Next, we're entering a large group of trees, which people of earth will call "woods."

Harry: Look at those trees Henry! They must be 1000 feet tall! These woods are so huge that a person wouldn't guess that he's within the walls of a city. I bet it's safe in here.

Henry: I bet you're right.

Harry: These woods sure aren't like the weird forest we came through on the way to Professor Tuliphead's place. What a difference! I'd feel like I could lie down and sleep in here without worrying about being hurt by anything - especially that old windbag wizard. Am I right?

Camero: Nothing is ever hurt or destroyed in the city of the Great King. There has never been any such thing here as death or pain. We're coming out of the woods now. We're are on our way to Mount Zion.

Henry: Mount Zion? You mean there's a mountain inside this city?

Camero: Yes.

Harry: This city must be bigger than New York.

Camero: In your present time frame, New York doesn't exist yet, but when it does, it will be tiny compared to this. There's Mount Zion just ahead of us. On top of it is a magnificent temple, and around it are seven other mountains.

Henry: What are on those other mountains?

Camero: Roses and lilies. To save a little time, I'll fly us to the top of Mount Zion. Here we go.

There's the temple below us. As you see, there are all kinds of trees around it to make the place beautiful. There are the Boxwood, Pine, Fir, Pomegranate, and Fig trees.

Henry: Look Harry, these trees are loaded with the largest figs I've ever seen. If it's alright with you, may I taste one?

Camero: Those who eat of this land go back to earth no more. Only those who live here may eat of this fruit. But soon, I will teach you how you may be able to live here and eat of that fruit. Would you like that?

Harry: We would love it! Whoops. Listen to me Henry. I can't believe I just said that. A while ago, I wanted to go home to earth. Now I feel at home. Who all is going to live here? I have so many questions!

Camero: They'll all be answered. First, I want to show you some other things. As you can see, this temple is supported by seven pillars - all of transparent gold, exquisitely set with lovely pearls.

Harry: Man! The greatest billionaires on earth are like street-people who live in a dumpster compared with those who live here. Did I say "are?" I meant "were." Ah - maybe I should say "will be." I forgot that the people we were with in the past are still in the future. It's kinda' crazy.

Look over there Henry, I see gold and silver all over the place!

Henry: To say nothing of the rubies, sapphires, diamonds, and other gems I've noticed.

Camero: Those aren't the most important things here. There is something else that the Great King and the Great Prince value much more than those things.

Harry: The Great Prince? Who is that? You never mentioned him before.

Camero: I haven't mentioned him because he is inside of this temple. I wanted to surprise you. When we go in here, you will see him for yourselves. I want to introduce him to you.

First, let me say that since we have come out of the woods, you have been seeing millions of messengers like myself flying in and out of the center of this city.

Henry: Yes. Since they look just like you, we figured that we knew who they are.

Look over there Harry! What an amazing fountain! It must be bigger than Niagra Falls! It's shooting hundreds of feet up in the air! Look at those colors! At the top, it's all white, red, blue, green, and then goes out into sparkles of shimmering colors that have no names in our language. That's got to be the most terrific fountain I've ever seen!

Camero: That fountain is beside the river of life - which you see running close to it. Those who drink of it, will never die.

Henry: Cool! In school we learned about some man in Florida who was looking for something like that. No wonder he never found it! There's no way he could have gotten here! I really don't know how we got here ourselves.

To tell the truth Harry, I think I'd be happy to just stay right here. We have more than any wizard or billionaire had on the earth when we left it.

Camero, most people where Harry and I came from have no idea that such a place as this exists. I've heard some wacko people talk about a place they called "heaven." But I didn't believe that there was such a place because of the coo coo way they acted. If there is a place called "heaven," it couldn't be any better than this!

Camero: There is no place in the universe that has more joy, peace, happiness or beauty than the city of the Great King. The main attractions here are the Great King and the Great Prince.

We are approaching the entrance of the temple now. Before we enter, let me say that you are going to see the things that are in the various rooms. You are going to see the Great Prince, and will be able to see what He is doing.

Henry: This is almost too good to be true. Is the Great King in this gigantic temple too?

Camero: He is.

Harry: Will we be able to see him too?

Camero: No. You cannot see Him now, but you may see Him in the future if you meet the conditions. I'll explain the reason for that at the proper time. Everything must come in its proper time.

Harry: Why can't we see him now?

Camero: You will learn the answer to that when we enter the temple. Come, follow me closely as we enter.

Inside the temple, the boys see the great Prince and what He was doing. They see things that no human language can describe. When they come out, they stand in awe - trembling, and silent.

Henry: Will you be able to describe to anyone on earth what you saw in there Harry?

Harry: No way. I'm overwhelmed. I've never felt such awe. I've never seen such beauty. I've never heard such music. I've never smelled such fragrances. I've never felt so happy. I'm still shaking. While we were in there, did you see that blinding light coming from around a corner from another room?

Henry: Yes. Camero said that it encircles the Great King. That light seemed to come straight for me. As it came near me, I trembled and shook like a leaf. I thought that if it came any closer I would be struck out of existence. But the light passed me. Then I had some sense of the awesome power of the Great King.

To make the universe we passed through at warp speed - someone would have to have more than "superpower." He would have to have "all" power.

Camero: That is correct. Are you ready to go?

Henry: Where are we going?

Camero: I thought that you might like to take a little trip to visit one of the other planets.

Henry: You mean there are people on other planets?

Camero: Of course. Though planet earth doesn't yet exist, would you think that your world would be the only inhabited planet, with so many hundreds of billions of galaxies, constellations, and solar systems? You yourselves have come many trillions of light years through the vast cosmos. You were overwhelmed with its greatness. Would you think that someone as powerful as the Great King would make only one tiny planet in such a boundless universe? Oh no. He has a large family. Very large. Your planet and solar system will be only one of many billions. It will be located on one of the outer arms of the Milky Way galaxy, and will be so small that if it were to vanish from sight, it would be missed in the universe no more than if a tiny leaf fell from one small tree in a vast forest.

Henry: Amazing! By the time Harry and I left earth, no one had been able to get outside of our solar system. The scientists said that we evolved on the earth over billions of years so that we all came "from goo to you through the zoo." But I always wondered about that theory. Now I see that some "wise guys" made those theories up out of their own tiny heads. Even on the earth when we came from it, nature was in such balance and was so beautiful {except where man had messed it up} that I often wondered why many of those scientists didn't think that someone planned the beauties of the world - and that it didn't just come out of nowhere by "accident."

The great "brains" of our planet said that the world came from what they called a "big bang." They said that billions of years ago, all the matter in the universe was together in one tiny little spot. They say that it suddenly blew up and has been going farther out into space ever since - - and that the earth, and everything else in the universe came from that exploded matter after it cooled off. But when I asked any of them where that mass of matter came from in the first place before it blew up, they could never tell me. When I asked them how the great mass of matter was made from nothing, they tried to change the subject. When I asked them if anything can come from the nothingness of nothing without being made, they got upset. Their dumb bang theory really didn't answer anything - because according to them, the same amount of matter and energy existed before the explosion, as after it.

Harry: How could millions of us have

swallowed such a farce all these years?

Camero: To swallow, one must first be fed. But come, let's go now on a little journey together. Before I intercepted your flight through space, your journey was uncontrolled. Now, I will guide you. Here, put these on. I have a pair for each of you.

Henry: Wings! Why do we need wings when we can already fly?

Camero: You've been flying along with me faster than the speed of light within the sphere of my aural influence. Now, when we get to another planet, you will be able to fly with these wings at slow speed - like the birds - by your own ambient power. You'll also be able to fly faster than the speed of light when you need to.

Camero helps the cousins put on a pair of special wings. They walk out one of the gigantic gates until they are standing on the outside of the city - peering out through the sterilized "Vacuum," into deep space.

Camero: Do they feel alright?

Harry: They feel fine.

Henry: Look at that gate Harry. I didn't notice it so much when we came in. What's it made of? It looks like it's made of one gigantic pearl.

Camero: That is correct.

Henry: Does it mean anything special that these gates are each made out of a giant pearl?

Camero: Yes. On your way back to the earth, you will learn all about the meaning of the pearl.

Harry: How?

Camero: I could tell you now, but I want you to learn it in a way that will help you the most. I want you to see these things with your eyes as well as hear of them. Then you will actually experience them, and be able to sing of them with the choir.

Henry: Choir! What choir?

Camero: There is to be a special choir that

will sing of their experience. It will be the largest, and greatest choir that has ever lived. The sound of that choir will be so great that the arches of this great city will vibrate and ring with the sound as it goes out past the gates into the boundless reaches of the universe.

Harry: Awesome!

Henry: Yes, we'd love to be in that choir. If the songs we sing are the songs of our experiences, then I understand why you can't just tell us everything right away. I see why you've got to let us see and experience these things as we go back to earth. Thanks for telling us about the choir anyway.

Harry: Does that great choir exist now?

Camero: It will exist after the earth is made. You'll learn more about that later.

Henry: Is there a choir in the city now?

Camero: Yes. When we get back from our visit to another planet, you'll hear it for yourself. It's the greatest choir in the universe at this time. It is made up of billions of us messengers.

Harry: Wow! I'm sure that this great choir has

a conductor. Is it the Great Prince?

Camero: No, it is conducted by the great and beautiful messenger who is next in authority and power to the Great Prince.

Henry: What's his name?

Camero: His name is Cosmo. But come, let's go now on our journey to another planet. I think that you'll enjoy visiting with some of the inhabitants there.

Henry: I've never flown with wings before. How do I know I won't crash?

Camero: I'll teach you the moment you start. Just follow me, and you'll know perfectly how to fly right away. At first, we'll go slow. Then, as you get used to the feel of your wings, we'll speed up to the speed of light. Just keep me in sight. Don't get too far behind and you'll be alright. In fact, I'll go along beside you for a ways. Would that make you feel better?

Henry: Yes.

Camero: Alright, here we go.

The three pass through the clear space stretching 50 million miles from the gates of the city. After coming out of the "Vacuum," they now accelerate to warp speed - going so fast that they disappear as they streak across the emptiness of endless space.

After a few minutes, they slow as they approach a beautiful colored galaxy shaped like a pinwheel.

Camero: Follow closely now. We're going into the middle of an inner arm of this galaxy. We'll go right through the arm - between thousands of its suns, and solar systems to a planet that I want to show you.

In - - in they flash. All of a sudden they land on a grassy hill by a beautiful lake.

Harry: Camero, on the way in, I noticed that this planet has seven moons.

Camero: That's right.

Henry: Wow! It's so bright and gorgeous here! It's almost as lovely as the city.

Harry: This is amazing Henry. Look at this. The grass here is living green, and look at those birds! They're warbling such a sweet song that it's like they have great intelligence. There's music everywhere.

Henry: Look over there! Ha ha! There's a flock of those birds flying together with a blend of yellow and red - bending through the sky like a singing flame of fire!

Harry: Mmmmmmmmmm! Smell those flowers! We're out in the country Henry, but I see some people way over there. Are they people?

Camero: Yes. There are billions of people who live on this planet. In fact, this planet is larger than your earth will be when it is made. Your minds can't fathom it. There are hundreds of billions of galaxies with hundreds of billions of solar systems in each one, and most of those solar systems have planets with billions of people on them."

Henry: You gotta love it! Us poor earthlings

used to wonder if there might be life on one or two other planets somewhere. Our heads needed to be expanded. They were as thin as a razor blade. Someone found a rock which someone said may have fallen down from Mars. When the scientists scoped it, they found what looked like it could have been some kind of a molecule. Then everyone got all excited. If they could only get a glimpse of this place! We thought we were so smart. With our drugs, junk food, tobacco and alcohol, we were killing ourselves, and thought we were happy!

After seeing this place, I wouldn't even want to say what people were turning the earth into. If the kids in my neighborhood could be here for just one minute, they'd never want to leave!

Harry: And the music!

Henry: Yea! We used to listen to junk that sounded like a dozen drooling apes from the darkest jungles screaming and beatin' on garbage cans. Everyone hailed it as "great."

Listen! I hear music coming from somewhere. It's kinda like what we heard in the city. I've never heard anything like it. It almost sends chills down my back. Listen to that harmony!

Camero: Let's go over and talk with some of these people.

The three fly slowly just above the treetops and land in front of some "people" who were having a picnic lunch beside a lake. They look different than humans from earth, being of different sizes and shapes. But they are noble, majestic, and are more beautiful than earthlings.

The boys are not afraid of them. They seem overjoyed as they talk with one, and then another and another.

Henry: I hope we're not bothering you while you're eating.

Orbison: Not at all! We're happy that you've come to visit us. What galaxy are you from?

Henry: We're from the Milky Way. But this planet is the most beautiful place I've ever seen - except for the city of the Great King. Have you ever been to the city?

Orbison: Oh yes. I've been there many times. We get to visit on certain special occasions. We love to see the Great King and the Great Prince. We love to roam around the city and hear the massive messenger choir. There's so much to see and do in the city! It contains things that you'll not find anywhere else in the universe.

Henry: You guys must be some of the luckiest people in the world. Ah, I mean in the universe.

Harry, these people are so kind. I see them always doing stuff to make each other happy. They don't look like us, but their faces are beaming with joy.

Harry: Yea, I bet they wouldn't hurt a flea. Camero, do these people have laws on this planet like on the earth when we came from it?

Camero: Yes, they do have laws, but only a few. They don't have all the many thousands of laws that you had, because they don't need them.

Harry: Like what?

Camero: They don't have laws which prohibit them from throwing garbage or trash on the landscape, because they have no garbage or trash. They have no laws limiting their speed. With their wings they may fly anywhere at whatever speed they wish. They have no crashes, so they have no emergency rooms. They have no fire departments because they don't need them. There is no crime - so they have no policemen. They eat only the natural things that grow from the ground - which contain all the nutrients they need. For that reason, they never get sick, and they kill no animals. They are many thousands of years old, but, as you see, they always look young. There are no poisons on this planet, or any of the planets of the universe, so there are no laws regulating them. They have no fire arms, so they need no gun laws. They don't need motor vehicles, so they need no traffic laws. These people obey the natural laws of health which the Great King has given them. None of them have ever died. They have no pain. They have never cried because none of them have ever been sad. There's nothing here to make them sad. Everyone on these planets are happy because they are kind and unselfish. They find joy in making each other happy. That is the supreme law of the universe that the Great King has made.

The boys' mouths are hanging open.

What Camero is saying seems so strange that Henry and Harry talk with the people and ask them if these things are true. Their eyes are big as they hear the people tell of the peace, love, happiness, and safety that everyone on the planet has. The cousins ask question after question to their new, fascinated friends. Henry laughs when he hears that there are no speed limit signs because there are no speed limits; no seat-belt laws, because there are no seat-belts; no hospitals, because there is no sickness, and no cemeteries, because there is no death.

Henry: Do you guys know about cars or trucks?

Pelegra: What are they?

Henry: I should have known. Uh, they are vehicles to get around on.

With a laugh, the beautiful Pellegra asks why they would want something to get around on when they can fly faster than the speed of light, or hover in the air - or go wherever they wish at any time - instantly!

Henry: Ahhhhh. Yea, I guess that was kind of a dumb question. It sure is a lot prettier here without those slow, clumsy cars anyway.

Harry: And quieter too. I don't hear any honking, or squealing of tires.

Henry: I don't see or smell any smog, or exhaust fumes, or hear noises of police cars, or ambulances, or fire engines, or screaming, or crying, or anything. I hear the breeze, and the birds, and that gorgeous music coming from somewhere. And I smell the most lovely flowers. This place is full of flowers!

Harry: Maybe we shouldn't even bother them with our primitive questions from the future dark ages.

Henry: Future? Yea, I guess you're right. People where we came from are like cave men compared to these powerful people. I keep forgetting that the earth doesn't exist yet. I think I want to just ask them one more question Harry. I know that Camero mentioned it, but I want to hear it from one of them.

Ah, excuse me sir. It looks like you people are

about 12 to 15 feet tall. Have any of you on this planet ever died?

Harry: From the look on their faces, I can tell that we can forget that Henry. This place is not like where we came from - - that's for sure. Do you comprehend this Henry?   There's no suffering in this place! And what about all the other zillions of planets?

Camero: They are the same.

Henry: How can we tell whether these people are male or female?

Camero: They are neither.

Henry: What? Without being male and female, how do they have babies?

Camero: They don't. They are like us messengers. All the planets are the same.

Harry: Then how did they all get here?

Camero: They got here the same way as we messengers got here. They got here the same way the great city, and the entire universe got here.

Harry: Oh I see! I don't think the scientists where I came from would like that explanation. The idea of having the universe filled with people who never die and never have babies might make them go crazy. It would blow away their theories. It's probably good that they don't exist yet anyway.

Henry: Harry, I never thought I'd say this, but I think I'd be happy to just live right here, or in the city.

Harry: Me too.

Camero: You both were so anxious to go back. Now you've changed your minds. But I don't blame you. Nevertheless, you must go back to the future earth. After it comes into existence, you have a work to do there.

When you left it, the earth was "messed up" as you say, yet, you are going to see that planet earth will have a special place that no other planet will ever have. It is going to be the most special planet in the universe. Soon you'll understand why.

Harry: When we go back to the future, and the earth is made, are we going to work in any way with you messengers?

Camero: Yes. But most of time you won't see us.

Harry: What will we be doing?

Camero: You'll learn that later, but meanwhile, you have more to learn in the city. We're going back there now - so follow me. Here we go.

Like three dazzling flashes of lightning, Camero, Harry, and Henry again fly at warp speed straight through the middle of the galaxy - past billions of stars, planets, suns, nebulas, and flaming systems - back to the city of the Great King.

Within the "empty" 50 million mile space outside the city walls, they slow to the speed of light which will bring them to the walls in about 4 minutes. While traveling at this slower pace, another messenger, like a streak of blinding light approaches the three. He flies by the side of Camero, and after a moment of communication, streaks away. They are only about 10 million

miles outside the walls {about a minute's flight}, when Camero speaks to the cousins again.

Camero: I've just received a shocking message that I must share with you after we enter the city.

Chapter Four

"The Revolt"

After entering the city through one of the twelve, immense gates, the three stand just inside the 275 foot high, pure gold, transparent walls. Camero instructs the boys to stay there for a little while as he goes to talk with other messengers to find out more perfectly what is going on. When he returns to the boys, Camero, for the first time - looks sad. He tells them the unbelievable news that one of the messengers has rebelled against the Great King! The whole city has gone into shock.

Camero: Boys, I must tell you the sad news that Cosmo has made it clear to everyone in the city that he is rebelling against the Great King and the Great

Prince. Since we have been gone, he has already tricked many of the other messengers into rebelling with him! The beautiful and peaceful City of the Great King is in chaos.

Harry: I don't believe this! It can't be! While you were gone, I noticed messengers streaking here and there, but I didn't know what to think. In a magnificent and happy place like this? - - This can't be!

Henry: The Great King is so kind and loving! He gives everyone everything they could possibly want. What kind of fool would rebel against Him - here in the center of the universe - of all places!? And why?

Camero: Let me tell you a little about Cosmo. He is not only the most beautiful, most powerful, and most talented of us all, but he also holds the highest position of anyone in the universe. He is next in authority to the Great Prince himself. You've heard the one hundred million member choir.

Harry: Oh yes!

Camero: Cosmo was leading it. He is the choir director. But that's not all. His position is so high that he stands right in the immediate presence of the Great

King inside that temple where I took you.

Henry: Yes, that's when I thought that intense light was going to knock me out of existence for sure.

Camero: Cosmo stands in the middle of that awesome light. That's part of his work. He walks right up into the mysterious multi-colored glowing, stones of fire, and shields the massive and awesome radiation emanating from the Great King. That radiation is so powerful that it would blot out of existence anyone who should dare to come near the city uninvited. Cosmo has a special throne not far from the throne of the Great King.

But that is not all. When the Great King and his Prince have a special council meeting and desire to share their plans with the inhabitants of the universe, Cosmo is the first one to learn about it. He goes out from there to tell the news to the other messengers. Then they speed to all parts of the universe at warp speed to tell it to everyone on all the trillions of planets in the hundreds of billions of galaxies.

There is nothing that anyone could want, or do, or have - - that Cosmo cannot do or have. Beauty, talent, love, superpower - all are his.

He is the most loved of all the messengers. We all love him. He knows it. No one could be more happy than he. But alas! Cosmo has rebelled!

Harry: Why, oh why!!!

Camero: There's no reason for it Harry. It's a mystery that no one understands because there's no need for it. If there was a reason for it, it would not be a mystery.

The universe is in a crisis boys. There are three more factors that I will tell you concerning these horrors.

As they talk, the three see great commotion as millions of messengers streak here and there. Many of the messengers are seen in groups - hovering in the air above the fields of flowers, or above the waters of the lake. Some groups are on the snow white sand of the large lake-shore beaches with their waving palm trees. They have no time now to notice the sparkling waves splashing gently on the shore. Some groups are seen hovering in the air around the mountain peaks. All are in deep discussions and debates concerning the shocking thing that is happening.

Camero: Come, follow me. I'm going to take you to a great shining forest so we can be alone to talk. I don't want any of the followers of Cosmo to hear what I say to you right now.

The three fly to the forest at the foot of one of the delectable mountains, and land in a large area of green, waving grass surrounded by flowering fruit trees.

Henry: What a gorgeous place! It's so peaceful here. You'd never know of the frightening things happening in the city. It makes me want to cry.

Camero: Yes. I've seen many of the messengers weeping. I have wept too. But I'm trying to control myself so that I can explain to you boys what is going on. Here are some points I want to tell you.

Firstly, Cosmo learned that the Great King was going to work with the Great Prince to create a new and distinct planet with a highly honored order of beings on it. When Cosmo learned that our great Leaders didn't take him into that council meeting to plan this new planet, he got jealous and angry. Because of his high position in the kingdom, he thought that he should be consulted.

Secondly, when Cosmo found out that the Great King was going to make the people on this new planet in His own likeness, and that they would one day be able to enter into the secret council into which Cosmo cannot go, he got jealous of them too.

Henry: Did you say that the Great King is going to make a planet with beings on it that would look like himself?

Camero: That's right. The people on the other planets are very beautiful, as you have seen. They are different shapes and sizes, but they don't look just like the Great King. There are already trillions of planets, and the vast universe family is almost complete. But the Great King has made known to us that He wants to make one more order of being - the highest possible. He wants to make an order of being that will be so exalted, and perform a function so special, that they will be able to do what no one on any planet can ever do. They will be able to do what no messenger, including Cosmo, can ever do. They will be able to come from their planet - right into the city - like a wife on earth coming into her own home - and go right into the temple of the Great King, climb up the mysterious, glowing stones of fire, and sit on thrones with the Great King Himself - as His bride.

Henry: Wow.

Camero: Not only that, they will also take part in the secret council by which the universe is ruled. They will actually help to co-rule the universe boys! The Great King will share His plans with them. In fact, He will share everything with them just like a man shares things with his beloved wife in the earth system that you came from.

Not only will the people on this new planet look like the Great King and co-rule the universe with him, but the beings of this entire planet will be so close to him that in many respects they will share the relationship that a loving wife shares with her husband. No one in the universe has even heard of such a thing as this. No one knows what a husband or a wife is, because no one on any of the planets has ever had one. But I mention this to you because you know about such things from whence you came.

The entire universe is going to be filled with wonder when they learn how highly exalted this new planet is going to be.

Henry: Amazing! Absolutely amazing!

Harry: It sounds like this planet will be his wife - his queen!

Camero: You could say that. And Cosmo is jealous of them. He is furious over it. He wants no one to ever be higher than himself, or closer to the Great King.

Harry: If Cosmo wants to be so close to the Great King, then why did he leave his position in the immediate presence of the King, and go off to rebel?

Camero: That is part of the mystery that no one understands.

Harry: When Henry and I were in that gorgeous temple where the Great King was, we didn't see him, but we were told that if we did, we would cease to exist. That kind of power makes me tremble. If the order of beings on this new planet are going to look like him, what will they look like? What will be the name of this new planet?

Camero: Harry and Henry - - the people on this new planet will look like you!

Harry: What!

Camero: The new planet will be called 'earth.'

Henry: WOW!!! This blows my mind! As I think of the history of our planet {that doesn't yet exist}, and think about the condition that many of the people were in when we left, this gives me a funny feeling.

Harry: Us in the image of the Great King!! Why? How could us shriveled up dwarfs deserve such honor? Out of all the beings in the universe, why would He choose us people from earth to make us to look like himself! How can this be?

Camero: You'll learn the answers to those questions as you see the unfolding of things. But now we have a crisis here. A terrible crisis. Cosmo knows that one day, you from earth will be greater and more exalted than he. He cannot tolerate the thought. He is furious over it.

But that is not all. As I mentioned, He is also

jealous of the Great Prince.

Harry: What does the Great Prince have to do with all of this?

Camero: Cosmo is jealous of the Great Prince because not only is he in the secret council where Cosmo cannot go, but he is going to work with the Great King in bringing this new planet into existence, and Cosmo will have nothing to do with it.

Henry: Jealousy in the Great City? What a shame! How could it be?

Camero: That's just the point. It's new. It's unexplainable. It's mysterious.

Harry: How will the Great Prince make the new planet?

Camero: You will soon see the answer to that with your own eyes. You boys have the privilege - which other earthlings have never had - - to see the future before it happens. As you see what is about to happen, it will answer many questions that you've had - - eternal questions of life and death. And when you are brought back to the earth in the future, you will be able to help others because of what you have learned.

Look over there. There are thousands of messengers in commotion. There's Cosmo now. I've learned that many are getting the feeling that there will soon be a confrontation between him and the Great Prince. The two have been together for a long time as best friends. All the planets know of their close relationship. They don't understand the words of Cosmo against his kind and gentle Friend. Since we returned from our visit to the other planet, I was told that Cosmo has been making insinuations against the Great Prince. What is really sad is that Cosmo actually has been gaining millions of sympathizers. Nearly every hour, more of my dear friends are joining him, and are turning against our kind and loving Prince. We truly are in a terrible crisis boys. I must do all in my power to help the messengers to not be fooled by him. I'm going to leave you to go and talk with as many of them as I can. The false arguments of Cosmo are so tricky that many of the messengers don't realize that if they follow him, the result will end in terrible disaster. No messenger, however powerful, can successfully fight against the Great King. He spoke them into existence. If He wanted to, He could make them disappear. But He is not like that. His great love for us causes Him to bear long with Cosmo.

Unfortunately, that very mercy and patient love is making Cosmo more bold. It seems that he is trying to take advantage of the kind nature of the Great King, to get his own way. He is thinking that if he presses his issues hard enough and long enough, the Great King will give in to him, and that he can rule all the billions of messengers in the city with the same authority that the Great Prince does.

Henry: Did you say billions?

Camero: Yes, there are billions.

Harry: All in this city?

Camero: That's right. The city is vast - a fitting capitol for the King of the universe. As you saw, even the great temple where He lives is so massive that many hundreds of millions of us can stand in front of His throne.

Listen. Cosmo is starting to speak to a great assembly over there. Stay here a little longer. I'm going to go over to see what he has to say. We were gone when all this started, and I want to get fully informed as to what is happening.

After a while, Camero comes back and informs the boys more fully as to the shocking things that are going on. He learns that to all appearances, the intention of Cosmo is to lead his followers in a great revolt.

Camero: I've heard Cosmo speak, and some of the other messengers have also filled me in. The problem is greater than I feared.

As I looked at him, I remembered that Cosmo has always been very happy. His form is perfect. He is noble and majestic. A special light has beamed in his face, brighter and more beautiful than around all the other messengers. Yet the Great Prince is above him, and is next to the Great King.

Cosmo can't stand the thought of him being inferior to the Great Prince. He's so jealous that he can't take it any longer.

Harry: Doesn't he remember that it was the Great Prince who made him?

Camero: It seems that his insane jealousy is making him blind to many things that he should remember. He is so filled with rage at this point that if anyone were to remind him of what you just said, it would just make him more angry. He has always been happy with his great and high position, but now - for no real reason, he is not. Even now, he is fomenting thoughts against our Prince in the minds of many millions of the messengers in the city. What is so sad is that many of them are believing him, and are joining him in this insane rebellion! I see a terrible revolt coming. Even war.

Henry: Horrors! I still don't see why he's rebelling. Why should he be jealous of the Great Prince, or of anyone? What more could Cosmo want? He has everything that anyone could ever want, including love!

Camero: That's right. Everyone loves him. He has everything - power, fame, love, riches. His body is covered with jewels and precious stones. He sparkles and shines like a dazzling flash of lightning. There is no created being in the universe more perfectly beautiful than he. His rebellious whisperings are very mysterious.

Harry: I hear thunder.

Camero: Listen. The Great King is summoning the billions of us to come and stand before Him in the outer court of His temple. I must leave you now. But first, follow me to a lovely home by the lake.

The boys fly with Camero over hill and shining forest to the shore of a glimmering blue lake with a pure white, sandy beach.

Camero: Until I return, you'll have everything that could be desired. Make yourselves at home. I'll be back as soon as I can. Then I'll fill you in on what's going on.

Camero stays away from the boys for quite a while this time as he hears what the Great King says to all the messengers, including Cosmo.

In amazement, Camero watches the unfolding of events. When he returns, his tear-stained face reveals his strong emotions. Camero fills the boys in on what has been going on in the newest turn of this horrifying development.

The boys are sitting on the front porch by the peaceful lake, surrounded by swaying palm trees, white sandy beach, grass, and flowers. The tiny white waves lap on the shore in a song of joy that seems to mock the benumbing terror that everyone feels. Suddenly Camero zips up in a dazzling flash of light, and sits beside them.

Camero: Hi boys. Here's what's happening. The great King assembled everyone so that in their presence, He might set things straight in the minds of everyone, including Cosmo. His false accusations made it necessary for the Great King to remind all messengers of the fact that He used the Great Prince - in cooperation with Himself - to speak Cosmo, and all of us into existence.

At this vast assembly, the statement by the Great King left no doubt in anyone's mind that he has his Prince to sit on the throne with himself, and that they rule the universe together. Though Cosmo is the most powerful and greatest being ever made, he needs to understand that the Great Prince made him, and that he is not equal to him in power and glory, and never will be. He is in a totally different category, and after the

Great King finished speaking with us, it is now seen that Cosmo's jealousy of the Great Prince has no foundation. There's no reason for it.

Henry: Cosmo has been so powerful and honored that maybe he needs to learn how to be humble. Maybe this is his test.

Camero: Maybe you are right.

Henry: Oh, I wish that all of this wasn't happening! What has happened to Cosmo's brain? Has it gotten warped?

Camero: At the great assembly, the Great Prince was seated on the throne with His Father, and all the messengers were gathered around them. There were billions of us. It was awesome. The Great Prince is invested with authority to command the messengers, and all the planets as co-creator.

But even after all of that, I have to sadly tell you that Cosmo was still jealous. It seems that his envy of the Great Prince is making him to be in danger of going insane. He wants His power, but not His sweet, unselfish character.

Yet when all the messengers bowed to

acknowledge the supremacy, and rightful rule of our Prince, Cosmo bowed with them, pretending to be sincere. When we bowed, the ceaseless beams of glory went out from the Great King and His Prince over us. We felt their power. It was awesome. We felt their love. We bowed on our faces in love and deep respect as the dazzling and overwhelming light filled the vast temple, and burst out into the city - out past the walls, and into the universe itself. But even in the very presence of all that terrific power and love, the heart of Cosmo was filled with envy and hate.

Cosmo is determined to have equal power. He seems to have no gratitude even after the Prince has done everything possible to make him happy.

Harry: It seems like the more a person has, the more he wants - and the more unhappy he is!

Camero: Yes. Cosmo has gloried in his own loftiness, but he is not satisfied. Selfish ambition is never satisfied. Cosmo has thought - "Why should the Great Prince be honored above me?"

Now, Cosmo has made a hostile move. He has left the immediate presence of the Great King - filled with senseless envy against his best friend.

Boys, I have told you of two factors of contention that Cosmo has against our great Leaders. Here is the third one. It is that Cosmo has been whispering around the city that there is something wrong with the government of the Great King. He is insinuating that we messengers do not need the wise and good laws which have been set up by our Supreme Leader. He is secretly fighting against His law. He says that we are wise enough to rule ourselves without law.

Cosmo is so tricky that many of the messengers have been fooled by him. When he assembled them all to listen to him, he introduced his real subject - - himself.

Cosmo: Listen now to the great Cosmo! I have a message for you. I have been hurt. I have been grieved. The preference which the Great King gave to the Prince at that meeting - to the neglect of me, is not acceptable. From now on, all the sweet liberty that you have enjoyed is at an end. You are now slaves! That's right! The Prince is a slave driver who won't give me the power and honor I deserve! You can do what you want, but from now on, I will never again bow down to him. I will take the honor which I deserve and be the commander of all who will submit to follow me. I will give myself some new names. One of my new names will be Isis. Follow me and I will give you a life of freedom from law. I will give you freedom from the slavery of the Great Prince. Follow me, and I will make you kings!

Henry: Who will be fooled by these lies? Can't the messengers see through them? They are thousands of years old. They are smarter than I am! If I can see through his lies, why can't they? How could any of them fall for these things that are so plainly false?

Camero: Sadly, their love for Cosmo has blinded many of them. They are thinking that maybe there is something true in what he is saying. He is bewitching them. He is hypnotizing them. In His dealing with rebellion, the Great King can use only right and truth. Cosmo is using what our kind King cannot - - flattery and lies. He is twisting the King's words and claiming that it is not right for him to give laws and rules to everyone in the universe. Cosmo is saying that our kind and great King is only trying to exalt Himself.

Therefore it must be demonstrated before all the worlds as well as before the billions of messengers in the city that our King's government is just, and his law perfect. Cosmo is trying to make it appear that he himself is seeking to promote the good of the universe in his tricky rebellion. Therefore, the true character of the liar, and his real object, must be understood by all. That will take time. Cosmo must have time to show himself for what he really is - by his wicked works.

NOW there is great commotion! Cosmo and his sympathizers are going all over the city, trying to "reform" the government of the Great King!

Messengers who are loyal and true are seeking to bring Cosmo to his senses. With strong reasoning many messengers are seeking to convince Cosmo that he has no less honor now than he had before that meeting. They are making it clear that the mild, loving authority of the Great Prince has never been questioned, and that He has given no commands but what we all enjoy obeying.

Many of the loyal messengers are weeping. What terrors are just ahead of us, we do not know. But it seems that a horrible battle may come any time. Things are tense.

The terrible crisis has come to a head.

After all the pleading of the loyal messengers, Cosmo is fuming. He flashes around the city and calls together many millions of the messengers. They are hovering in the air above vast fields and plains of waving grass at the outskirts of the city - hundreds of miles from the temple. But Cosmo doesn't know that One is inside the city weeping. He knows not that One is hearing all, seeing all. He knows not that from the inside of the great and calm temple, One sits amid the blinding, staggering glory of radiation and light - - with tears, and a breaking heart.

Cosmo: You are slaves. I will submit no longer to this violation of your rights, and mine! We must fight for our rights! We can have a better government! Follow me, and I will give you the freedom you want. I will give you freedom from law. Follow me, and you will be free to do as you please. You can come and go as you please. No more restrictions. No more laws. No more rules. Live it up! Make me your supreme ruler, and I will give you all.

His words echo past millions of the

listening heads of powerful and shining messengers who love him. But some are perplexed. He doesn't care any more who hears him. His whispering days are over. Loyal messengers lift their voices and plead with Cosmo again, but he turns from them with a sneer.

Cosmo: You are deluded slaves.

They stand in amazement as they see that his efforts to excite rebellion are successful. They see great numbers - hundreds of millions - accepting Cosmo as their leader and chief commander. As he sees his success, Cosmo flatters himself that he will yet have all the messengers on his side - and then all the trillions of worlds on his side. He will be greater than the Great King himself! He imagines that his voice of authority will be heard in commanding the entire universe!

All of a sudden, one of the messengers lifts his voice above the vast throng and speaks out.

Allera: Please Cosmo! Listen to reason! I assure you that the consequence of your insane revolt against our kind and just King is that you will plunge yourself, and all who follow you into eternal death. Annihilation! Do you comprehend that? Can you sustain the universe Cosmo? Did you make it? Can you hold the electrons in their orbits? Can you guide the neutrinos and all the sub-atomic particles in the universe? Who do you think you are? He who spoke us all into existence by his mighty power can overturn your insane rebellion! You have called us slaves, but you are a slave to your own blindness. Do you think that we're feeble-minded? We are not the morons you are hoping we are. You are trying to put doubt into our minds about the kindness of our supreme Leaders. You are trying to make the plain and simple things that they say to be shrouded in mystery. The real mystery is how so many of us have swallowed the lies you've been dishing out against our kind Prince and our King. We aren't blind enough to think that a being like yourself can resist his good and just laws. For you to try to trick us into thinking that you can overpower the Great King and his Son, and rule the universe in peace and happiness is too absurd for us to swallow. If you plunge yourself and others into the hopeless darkness of death - to which you are heading - you will have only yourself to blame!

The loyal and true messengers continue to warn the others to close their ears to Cosmo's deceptive reasonings. They plead with them to go to their Great Leaders and confess their wrong of questioning their loving authority.

Many of Cosmo's supporters are thinking about taking this advise, and going to the Great King and Prince, and asking for forgiveness for doubting their love, and for siding with rebellion.

But now Cosmo shouts out to the vast throng.

Cosmo: I am acquainted with the law of the universe. If I should go back and submit to obey the Great Prince, my honor will be stripped from me. No more will I be intrusted with my exalted position. Not only that, all of you have now gone too far to go back. You are doomed with me. The Great King will not forgive you.

Henry: Even I know that that's a lie.

Cosmo: I will brave the consequences - for to bow to the Great Prince, I never will. We must assert our liberty and gain by force the position and authority which has not been given to us.

He's the same person, but yet he's not the same. His face has changed. His look is fierce. Something strange is happening to this super messenger - once so happy and peaceful. So far as Cosmo himself is concerned, it's true that he has now gone too far to return. But not so with those who have been blinded by his lies. To them the entreaties of the loyal messengers open a door of hope. If they will only follow their warnings of love, they can break away from the horrible snare that is leading them to a death in which is no hope of life, to a night to which comes no morning. Will they do it? Will they save themselves from ruin? It's not yet too late.

Pride, love for their leader, and the desire for unrestricted freedom are chosen, and the pleadings of love and mercy are finally rejected. Their minds are set. Their choice is final. Forever!

Camero: I joined the loyal messengers, and we went like lightning to the Great Prince to tell Him what is happening. I saw a look of pity on His face. I learned that He knew all about it, and has heard every word that has been spoken. When we got there, we learned that the Great King has been in conference with his Son concerning the best means by which the daring rebellion of Cosmo can be put down.

Harry: Oh my! What's going to happen? From the way Cosmo is talking, you'd think that he has power to attack his best Friend! What do you think will be the end of this awful thing? Will there be a battle? If so, what kind of weapons will Cosmo use?

Camero: The Great King has the power to hurl the liar from the city with a flick of His finger. But this is not his purpose. He will give the rebellious messengers an equal chance to measure their strength and might with his Son and his loyal messengers. In this battle every messenger must choose his own side. Yes Harry, there will be a battle. It will be terrible. But it is not safe to permit any who have united with Cosmo in rebellion to continue to remain in the city because they have learned the lesson of genuine rebellion against the unchangeable law of the Great King. Such insane rebellion in the face of such tender love is incurable. Through all of this ordeal, the messengers are being tested to see who will be loyal to whom. In their choice of leaders, they are choosing life or death. I've learned that soon, very soon, Cosmo and all who unite with him will be cast out of the Great City.

Henry: How?

Camero: You will soon see Henry. You will see the battle with your own eyes. It is the highest crime to rebel against the loving government of the Great King. The peace and happiness of the city - and the universe - demand that the trouble-makers cannot remain.

Chapter Five

"The Attack"

The entire city is now in terrible commotion.

Camero leaves the boys in a safe place to watch what is happening while he joins his comrades, as billions of messengers are marshaled into large companies, each division with a higher commanding messenger at their head.

Cosmo is warring against the law of the universe because he wants to exalt himself.

Now, before the massive armies join in battle, the vast host is summoned one last time to appear before the Great King to have each case determined.

Before the vast assembly, Cosmo madly thunders his dissatisfaction that the Great Prince should be honored before him, repeating the argument that he should be equal with him, and be taken into the secret council to understand everything, and help co-rule the universe.

Cosmo sees that the Great King makes no move to hinder or reprove him in his angry speech, and now his daring courage rises {in the face of humble but unlimited power}. Cosmo now yells out his fiery contempt for the law of the Great King. This Cosmo cannot bear. He claims that messengers need no law; that law is a restriction of their liberty, and that to abolish law is one great object of his standing as he does.

The messengers marvel at the patience of their kind and mighty King in the face of such insult. His majestic voice - like mild thunder, is now heard informing Cosmo that to His Son alone He will reveal His secret purposes, and that He requires all the family of the universe, even Cosmo, to yield implicit obedience; but that he has proved himself unworthy of a place in the

104

kingdom.

At these words, Cosmo is a super "madman." He whips his blazing robes around like a flame of fire, and exultingly points to his sympathizers - one third of all the billions of messengers in the great city. He is of dazzling brightness with a shining crown on his head. His gorgeous, jewel-studded robes flash and sparkle in the light coming from the throne of the Great King as he turns and points to the hundreds of millions on his side. With burning passion, he speaks to the King, and his words ring out over the billions of upturned heads - as he shouts his demands with fiery vehemence.

Cosmo: These are with me! Will you expel these also, and make such a gigantic hole in the empire? [Now he yells louder].

I am prepared to resist the authority of the Prince, and to defend my place in the city by force of might, strength against strength!

Loyal messengers are weeping. Tears are

running down their faces as they hear Cosmo's exulting boasts. The Great King now declares that the rebellious ones must remain in the city no longer. Their high and happy state has been held upon condition of obedience to the law of love which He has given to govern the high order of intelligences. But no provision has been made to keep in the city those who persist in rebellion.

Camero again flies quickly to the boys to fill them in on the latest developments and horrors.

Camero: Since the Great King has announced that Cosmo and the hundreds of millions of his followers must leave the city, loyal messengers are mourning their fate. Some don't realize yet that there is going to be an attack and a terrible battle. It could start any minute. Many of the loyal messengers are thinking of their love for Cosmo, and they mourn the fate of those who have been their friends in happiness. Their loss is going to be felt in the great city. All of this is hard for any of us to believe. Until Cosmo rebelled, everyone was happy.

Even now, no one really knows why this is happening.

All of a sudden - - Cosmo, with a mass of his messengers - attacks the Great Prince! ! !

It's a death thrust - aimed at his heart. Faster than the speed of light - loyal messengers intercept the deadly plunge.

There's war in the city! In the air - above the mountains - above the green flowery fields, above the lakes and beautiful beaches - above the streets - above the forests - above the city walls and gates - and out into the great, vast and empty "Vacuum" - like lightning flashes and tongues of fire - the battle rages. Faster than light, billions of warriors tumble and rage. A battle of friends. A battle "strange." Onward the battle moves. It pulses. It rages. It flows - exploding - bursting, flashing, blinding, tumbling - balls of fire.

The boys are terrified. They cover their faces. Fearful of the dazzling, startling explosions, they hold their hands over their eyes. They hold them tight - scared to look.

Finally -- they peek. They squint -- and, like great mountains of lightning - billions of flashing, erupting balls of fire are leaving the city - moving - out past the corridor of "Vacuum." Out, into the nothingness of space. And then - - - - - - it's over.

It's quiet. It's done.

They look around. They look at each other.

Harry: Whew! It's over. Where is everyone? The city looks empty.

The boys now see the Great Prince, followed by hundreds of millions of loyal messengers - streaming in through the gates. All is peaceful again. All is well.

Camero comes to the boys. His tear-stained face is calm.

Camero: We are going to miss them. I've known them for so long. We were dear friends. My heart goes out to them - out there in the blackness of space. I pity them. I love them. But they made their choice. The Great King gave them freedom to choose who they wanted for their leader. He gave them lots of time to make their final choice. They chose Cosmo. Their choice is final. A million more years wouldn't change their minds now. Their minds are fixed forever. My heart goes out to them. I know that they will be miserable out there. But there's nothing I can do. They're going to learn that to have Cosmo as their leader isn't like he said that it would be. They're going to learn that they have followed a great liar. They didn't take their chance to come back to loyalty to our kind and loving King and his Prince when it was offered them. Now rebellion is forever embedded in their hearts. If they ever got back into the city now, they would start up the terrible rebellion all over again. But that will never happen. The city is now safe. They will never enter its shining gates. There is peace once more.

Henry: What a relief! I feel sorry for them too. The empty blackness of space is such a horribly lonely place. They can keep each other company, but won't it be terribly boring out there with nothing to do? What will they do out there? Where can they go?

Camero: You'll soon see.

Now all the vast host of messengers gather around the Great King and his Prince. They bow in love and gratitude. Not a bit of rebellion is left in the city. All is peaceful as before.

Camero is soon going to take the boys many light years into space to see how Cosmo and his friends are doing. But first, he tells them what the Great King is planning.

Camero: Now boys, the Great King is

consulting his Prince in regard to carrying out their exciting plan of making the new planet with the special and most exalted order of being who will one day sit on his throne with him and be in the secret council.

Henry: Is the throne of the Great King large enough to hold all the people?

Camero: Yes. Now I am going to let you ethereally zoom out into space and take a look at Cosmo and his poor, miserable friends. We will see and hear them without them knowing about it.

Henry: What would happen if they saw us? Would they capture us and hold us as hostages?

Camero: Knowing how angry and frustrated Cosmo is right now, that is very possible. It would be dangerous to go anywhere near them now in a form that they could see.

The boys with Camero ethereally zoom in on a remote place into the emptiness of outer space called "Tartarus." Without being in danger of being captured by them, the boys can now see and hear what's going on with the great rebel and his many millions of restless, turbulent supporters.

Gamorra: Alright Cosmo. You promised us freedom. You promised us greater happiness and joy, and a more exalted state of being. So where is it! What kind of fools are we to follow you into this dark and awful place where there's nothing to do, and nowhere to go? What kind of brains did we have to think we could beat the Great Prince and two thirds of the messengers of the empire? Now we're bored - tooling around in this miserable darkness like the blind following the blind. Now we've all fallen into the ditch. What are you going to do about this Cosmo? Where are your great promises to us?

Cosmo stands in amazement at his new condition. His happiness is gone. He looks at the messengers who, with him, were once so happy, but who have been expelled with him from the beautiful city. Before their fall, they never had a shadow of sorrow. Now all is changed. Faces which used to be happy and joyful in close relationship to the Great King are now gloomy and hopeless. Strife, fighting, and bitter curses are among them. The great rebel chief is starting to see the terrible results of his rebellion.

He shudders. In earth terms, his great frame is about nineteen feet tall. He's shaking all over - afraid to face the future - afraid to think about the end of these things. To be ruler in the blackness of outer space is vastly different than being ruler in the lovely and peaceful city of light.

Zavetta: Here we are in the blackness of space Cosmo! We're having fun man!

Meanwhile, in the great city, the hour for joyful songs of praise to the Great King and His Prince has come. Cosmo had led the one hundred million member choir. In honor of their loving King and his Son, Cosmo had raised the first note, then the massive host united with him, making sublime and beautiful strains resound through the vast metropolis - vibrating the arches over the gates, and making them ring. But now, instead of sweetest music, curses fall on the ears of the rebel leader.

Where is he? Is this not all a horrible dream? The peaceful and beautiful city has always been his home. Is he shut out? Are the shining gates never more to open to let him into his own home?

Camero: Boys, the hour is drawing near when the billions of bright and loyal messengers bow before the Great King. I can see that if Cosmo could be again as he was when he was true and loyal, gladly would he yield up the claims of his authority. But for his mindless rebellion - he is doomed! And this is not all; he has led hundreds of millions of others to rebellion and into the same hopeless condition as himself. An awful responsibility now rests upon him from which he would gladly be released.

Henry: What will Cosmo tell his followers now? What will he do to make them happy and relieve their misery?

Camero: Nothing.

Henry: Nothing?

Camero: There is nothing he can do to keep his promise to make them happy. His boastful claims and promises to them were all a pile of lies. He has made a giant bed of misery for them all to lie in, and now they are in it.

Harry: Where will they all go? What will they do? Are they going to just go around in circles like a hundred million zombies on ski-jets, and be bored forever?

Camero: No. You'll see that their hatred will find a way to raise its ugly head. Never more will these unhappy beings be swayed by the mild and loving rule of the Great Prince.

Cosmo trembles. He trembles as he views his work. At warp speed, he zips off a few light years {a 10 second trip} into the blackness of space, just to be alone. The mightiest super-being ever made is by himself. There he is in the dark nothingness - alone. He wants to meditate on the past, the present, and his future plans. His giant body shakes like a leaf in a storm. A messenger from the city is passing nearby - on his way to a cluster of galaxies with news from the city. Cosmo calls him and begs for an interview with the Great Prince.

Of all wonders - this is granted!

Camero: Look boys, the Great Prince is leaving the city!

Harry: Where is He going?

Camero: He is going to Cosmo!

Henry: I can't believe it!

The heart of the Great Prince is breaking. His love for Cosmo is strong and hasn't changed. For many years, the two have been closest friends. They have walked arm in arm. The entire universe has known that there was no closer friendship than theirs.

Henry: Look Harry. Look at the face of the Great Prince. I've never seen such sorrow. I see a tears running down His face. It seems that from the way they're talking with each other, the terrible battle never happened.

Cosmo tells the Great Prince - {whom he had so recently attacked, and would have killed if he could have} - that he is sorry for his rebellion, and that he is willing to take the place which the Great King had given him before.

The Great Prince starts weeping out loud - holding his face in His hands. He weeps at Cosmo's sad condition. He weeps.

He wishes that He could just forget it all, and invite them all back into the city to be happy and joyful again - as if nothing had ever happened. He wants to do it. He craves to do it. He doesn't want to say what He has to say. It's so hard to tell Cosmo the truth. But He must.

Painfully He tells Cosmo that the seeds of rebellion are within him, and that He and the Great King know that if he was ever to be received back into the city, he would eventually start up the rebellion all over again.

Camero: Boys, Cosmo would not have been expelled if there was any hope that he would be obedient. But with the mysterious seeds of rebellion alive, growing, and wrapped around Cosmo's very heart like a horrible cancer, the peaceful city must not be placed in jeopardy by letting the chief rebel back.

Cosmo has not only hopelessly ruined himself, but he has ruined hundreds of millions of messengers who would have been happy in the kingdom had he remained loyal. Now those deadly seeds are growing in their hearts also.

Listen closely. If Cosmo and his friends were let back into the city, the time would come when they would again attack the Great Prince, and murder him if they could.

Not only that, since Cosmo and his sympathizers have crossed over the line into hopeless rebellion, if the rebels ever came back into the city, they would not only rebel again, but would cause more of the happy and innocent messengers to go into rebellion - who escaped Cosmo's terrible lies the first time.

Boys, you are going to see that Cosmo is not really sorry for His rebellion, or for his attempted murder of the Great Prince. He has betrayed a love for him that is so great that I don't understand it. If the great rebel should be brought into contact with the rest of the loyal messengers, or with the trillions of other planets, he would ruin as many of them as he could.

Cosmo is desperate. He is putting on an act to try to get back into the city. He is telling lies again.

Now, he is lying to the Great Prince. His love for Cosmo is just as strong and tender as ever, but He is not fooled by this attempt. He knows that he is being lied to. Cosmo is the first great "con artist." What he is sorry about is that he has lost his high position, and is now out in the blackness of space without a gorgeous place to live and work. He wanted to rule without the law of the Great King to restrict him. He got his wish. Now he can rule all he wants. Now he can rule over lawless, restless, unhappy beings that he himself has tricked, fooled, and ruined.

It is not possible that his love for the Great King and his Prince has increased so much since his fall that he would cheerfully submit to his law - which he has hated. He is miserable because he is realizing what he has thrown away, and because of his sense of horrible guilt for attacking and trying to murder his best Friend. Cosmo can't stand the thought of the loss of all the privileges and high honors he had in the city. It is driving him crazy.

When the rebel chief becomes fully convinced that there is no possibility of his being

re-instated in his position in the city, he erupts like a volcano. Like a chained lion, he roars out his fierce hatred with fiery vehemence. Exploding in a fit of anger - he would have killed the Great Prince on the spot had He not vanished from his sight.

NOW Cosmo flashes like a bolt of lightning in anger to one of the twelve gates of the massive and shimmering city.

Harry: What will he do? Will he kill the guards and crash his way through the gates?

Camero: He doesn't have the power to do that. His rage and supernatural strength are limited by the Great King so that Cosmo cannot hurt anyone who does not yield to his power. But the Great King knows that such determined rebellion will not remain inactive. Cosmo will invent means to harass the loyal messengers and show defiance. Look at him now. Since he is not able to kill or trick the tall messenger guards at the gates - or crash his way into the city, he is waiting just at the entrance. He's taunting the loyal messengers and seeking to pick a fight with them as they go in and out. Not only that, when the earth is soon made, Cosmo will seek to destroy the happiness of the people there. He knows that they will be a special order of being, and he will try to trick them into rebellion against the Great King so that they will be plunged into the same misery and future death that he is facing. He knows that that will cause grief to the hearts of our Great Leaders. He will now do anything to hurt them. Anything.

Harry: Will the Great Prince warn the people on the new planet about this dangerous rebel who'll try to ruin them?

Camero: Oh yes! One of us messengers will be sent to explain to them all about what has happened with Cosmo so they don't end up in the same horrible misery that he has plunged himself, and millions of messengers into.

Chapter Six

"The Planet"

A horrible monster is now loose in outer space. But even in view of this, the Great King and Prince immediately begin their mighty work of making the special planet - one so beautiful that it is to be the gem of the universe. It will have the highest order of beings of any world. It will truly be a "super-race" having features of the face which will look like those of the great Leaders of the universe. They have carefully planned the making of these beings - who will one day be sitting on thrones with the Great King Himself.

Harry: How will the earth be made? And why didn't the Great King just kill Cosmo and his fellow rebels so that there wouldn't be these monsters lurking around who are able to trick, hurt, or destroy the people on the new planet?

Camero: It is true that all suffering in the universe comes from the work of Cosmo and his army. It's also true that these murdering fiends are going to die one day and be turned to ashes. But you'll see later that if the Great King had killed Cosmo and his army right away, the rest of the universe would have served Him from fear and not from love. Cosmo has to be allowed to live long enough to show what his principles really are - so that when he will finally die, everyone will know that his death is an act of love for the universe - and even for Cosmo. All the messengers and all the worlds have to see clearly that he is a murderer and a liar.

The Great King could have destroyed Cosmo and his sympathizers as easily as one can cast a pebble to the earth; but He did not do this. Rebellion is not to be overcome by force. Compelling power is found only under Cosmo's government. The principles of our King are not of this order. His authority rests upon goodness, mercy, and love. Cosmo has used fraud and lies to get his way. His power to deceive is very great, and by disguising himself in a cloak of falsehood he has gained an advantage. Even the loyal messengers cannot yet fully discern his character or see to what his work is leading. Cosmo must be given time to show everyone what and who he really is.

In his dealing with evil, the Great King could use only right and truth. Cosmo could use what the King could not – flattery and lies. He has falsified the words of the King, claiming that he was not just in giving laws to rule the inhabitants of the universe, and that in requiring submission and obedience from His creatures, he was seeking merely to exalt himself. Therefore it must be demonstrated before the inhabitants of all the worlds that the government of the Great King is just, and His law perfect. Cosmo has made it appear that he himself is seeking to promote the good of the universe. The true character of the usurper, and his real object, must be understood by all. His own work must condemn him. Cosmo has claimed from the first that he is not in rebellion. The whole universe must see the deceiver unmasked.

Had Cosmo been immediately blotted from existence, the worlds, and some of the messengers would have served the Great King from fear rather than from love. Cosmo's influence would not have been fully destroyed, nor would the spirit of rebellion have been wiped out. Evil must be permitted to come to maturity. For the good of the entire universe through ceaseless ages Cosmo must more fully develop his principles, that his charges against the divine government might be seen in their true light by all created beings - - that the justice and mercy of the kind and loving King, and the immutability of His law might forever be placed beyond all question.

Concerning your second question - how the earth is to be made - the Great King and Prince will work together to bring the earth into existence by the awesome power of their word. Together, they will cause atoms and molecules to come from nothing. Electrons, protons, neutrons, sub-atomic particles, and everything that makes the atoms and molecules of all matter, will be formed from the irresistible energy of that voice. And as before, it will be the voice of the Great Prince who will do the talking.

Henry and Harry with their messenger guide, watch in amazement as the earth comes into existence before their eyes at the voice of the Great Prince. At first the world is dark - a gigantic ball of black, seething, water. But to their astonishment - glowing light, dry ground, lush green grass, trees, flowers, blue sky, rivers, lakes, beaches, and majestic mountains appear as day after day the Great Prince speaks.

Henry: Look Harry! At first there was just a black blob, but as the Great Prince keeps speaking each day, it's starting to look like that other gorgeous planet we visited.

Camero: Let me explain to you boys a little of what is happening. Under the ground are vast layers of rock which are serving as bones to the earth. Together, the Great King and Prince have arranged the lakes and seas in a very artistic manner to give the greatest amount of beauty. Also notice that the hills, mountains, and lovely plains are decorated with plants, flowers; and tall, majestic trees of every description, which are many times larger than they will be later in the history of the planet. I know that you don't understand why the trees will be smaller later, but you will understand more as things unfold.

Notice that the air is pure and healthful. The earth looks like a kingly palace.

Harry: I hate to keep using the word "gorgeous," but that's the only word I can think of to describe this.

Henry: I'll use the word "awesome."

Camero: Look up there in the sky! Hundreds of millions of loyal messengers are belting the earth to see it, and admire its beauty. We are all sightseers. None of the other planets have had such a welcoming committee as this. This is truly the most highly exalted planet in the universe!

Henry: Listen to them singing! Amazing! It looks like billions of them up there. I feel like singing too. It's great to see the earth again. It's great to be home!

Harry: Camero, what do you think Cosmo and his miserable friends are doing now? This is where the action is. I don't think there's anything out in space to interest him more than this, do you?

Camero: Cosmo and his fellow rebels are watching from way out in the darkness. With their powerful eyes, they can zoom in and see everything perfectly. I can see him now. He's looking at this beautiful world like a hungry lion would look at a new-born calf. In his state of mind, I know that he has plans for planet earth. He is planning to capture it, and turn it into his headquarters. If he can do that, then he will have a place to live and work - and won't have to stay out in the blackness of Tartarus with nothing to do. He could then use it as a base to fight against the Great King. From here, he could try to get the many billions of other planets on his side.

Boys, Cosmo is the first great terrorist. But you can be sure that the Great King and His Prince know all about his schemes. They will do all they can to thwart his frightening plans. But there is one thing that they will not do.

Harry: What's that?

Camero: They will not force the people of

earth - or any planet, to obey them. Earth people must be tested like we messengers were. The Great King will give people of earth a free choice to obey and follow him into life and eternal happiness, or to follow Cosmo into disobedience, despair, and death.

After the earth was brought into existence with its many varieties of fascinating and beautiful animals, birds, fish, lush trees and fragrant flowers, the Great King and Prince carried out their purpose, {which was made before the fall of Cosmo}, to make people on earth to look like themselves.

All of a sudden, a voice is heard that sounds like the waves of the ocean -

"Let us make man in our own image."

As Adam comes forth from the hand of his Maker, he is well proportioned. Adam is of great height, {about 16 feet tall}. His features are perfect. The look on his face is mild, and noble, like the faces of the loyal messengers. The head of the tallest basketball player of the 21st century

A.D. would come a little below Adam's waist. He could pick up a seven foot tall basketball player with one hand, and a 300 pound football player with the other. If Adam stood beside a fourteen foot, one story house, he could look down on the top of the roof. He would have to twist his body sideways to squeeze inside through the door, and would have to crawl inside the room on his hands and knees. But he could not fit inside unless the house had a large, 16 foot long living room. He would be stuck in that one room, and wouldn't have room to turn around. His massive body would mostly fill the entire room, and Adam would have to back out of the door that he came in. If he stood on a car, it would smash it down, and blow out the tires. It would take a large truck to hold him, but he could not fit inside.

The kingly Adam could jog down the freeways and keep up with the traffic. The sight of him would cause traffic jams. To see this giant thundering past them on the freeway would cause women to go screaming off the road into the ditch. If a car got in his way, he could pick it up and put it wherever he pleased.

The media and paparazzi would go wild. They would want to interview him, and see what he had to say. His picture would go by satellite to news agencies around the world.

Unfortunately, he would eventually have to travel on the back of a truck behind bullet-proof glass, because many in the 21st century, in jealousy, would want to kill him. If he was found alone, great masses of people would mob him. They would riddle him with questions. Gangs of evil men would try to wrestle him to the ground. If he fell on some of them, it would crush them. If he accidently killed any of them, he would be accused of being a dangerous wild creature, and would be captured by the authorities to be locked up. If he ran and tried to escape, helicopter gun ships would be sent to attack him. The media and society would go crazy as they tracked him down to shoot him with tranquilizer guns; wrap him up with large heavy chains, and take him by truck to a special room in a prison with thick bars, or to an elephant cage in a zoo surrounded by bullet-proof glass. For his own protection, and the good of others, it would be thought too dangerous to let him lose in society. He would be locked up, and viewed by the world as a giant monstrosity - pitied by the world, and those who loved him.

Henry: Adam is really handsome! He looks so kind and gentle. He would never hurt anyone.

Camero: That's right Henry. But many people from the world you came from would hurt him. If he were allowed to be free in that society, money leaders would be afraid that he might join a sports team. If that happened, it would wreck the entire industry. The tiny 350 pound football players would be to Adam like tiny pygmies. They would be scared of his massive body weighing over a ton. If he ran into any of the players, or stepped on them, their bones would be crushed. Many - where you came from in the 21st century didn't realize it, but their sports were mainly a big business, to make certain people rich from the fees they charge the fans, and advertisers. Adam would wreck their whole crooked business, and it wouldn't be long before someone would be hired to kill him. For his own sake, the kingly Adam would have to be viewed from behind bullet proof glass if he were alive in the earth's 21st century A.D.

Adam's complexion glowed with the rich tint of health. He was filled with joy, peace, and happiness. He was the healthiest man who ever lived - with a system made to never die.

Eve was not quite as tall as Adam. Her head reached a little above his shoulders. She, too, was noble--perfect in symmetry, and very beautiful. If she existed in earth's 21st century, the media would go insane. She too would have to be guarded day and night by a team of armed body-guards, and would have to live and travel behind bullet-proof glass.

Harry: Look Henry, Adam and Eve are giants. They're beautiful. I notice that they have no clothes on, but I can't see through the soft, beautiful light that surrounds them.

Camero: Yes. They are clothed with a covering of light like we messengers wear. While they live in obedience to the Great King, this circle of glowing light will always cover them. Although everything here is the perfection of beauty, yet He has tried to show his great love by planting a special garden just for them. Some of their time will be spent in the happy work of dressing the garden, and some of their time they will spend in receiving visits from us messengers. Their daily labor amid the trees, flowers and animals, will not be tiresome, but will be pleasant and invigorating. It seems that no one could ever be happier.

One thing that makes the earth so unique is that it is different than all the other planets in its dimensions. It is seven thousand, nine hundred and twenty seven miles in diameter at its equator. It rotates on its axis one complete turn every twenty three hours, fifty six minutes, and four point zero nine seconds. That makes one earth day. It goes around the sun every three hundred sixty five days, five hours, forty eight minutes, and approximately forty five seconds. That makes one earth year. Each week is made up of seven days.

After Adam and Eve are brought into existence, the Great Prince performs the first wedding ceremony. The boys look on in wonder at the scene. This ceremony takes place in the most lovely, gleaming garden that has been made for them. Soon after the ceremony, the sun goes down on the sixth day since the earth was made from the dark watery ball.

Now the seventh day begins, when the Great King and His Prince look over what they have made, and rest in their love - enjoying it - along with the entire onlooking universe. The planets of a hundred billion galaxies are rejoicing and shouting for joy. The King pronounces the earth "very good," and sets aside {as a love gift for man} this seventh day as a special, holy day of rest - to commemorate the creation of the world by the Great King and Prince of the Universe.

Camero: Notice boys that in the planet you came from, there were people who said - from their false "science" - that the earth took millions or billions of years to come into existence. And there were others who said that each day of the creation was a thousand years or more. But notice that the Great King and his Prince made the flowers, grass, and trees the day before he made the sun. Since the vegetation of earth can't live a thousand years or more without the sun, those people would blush if they knew the one simple fact that the Great King made the earth in six literal days, and rested on the seventh.

Harry: Hey! That's right! Camero, do you think that anyone on the other planets are jealous of the people here on earth, since they are in the image of the Great King himself, and are exalted higher than any of the other planets?

Camero: No Harry. They are not like Cosmo. No one on the other planets are jealous of the people of earth. Rather, they are happy for them. They are happy that they will one day have the privilege of co-ruling the universe with the Great King and Prince. They are expressing to each other a feeling of eager anticipation. Those on the other planets are happily talking of the day that they can meet their new "earth" friends in the great city on a visit. This sweet spirit of unselfish love shown by them is the spirit of life for the universe. It is the spirit that fills the city of the Great King. It is the spirit that Cosmo rejected. He chose the dark and unhappy spirit of selfishness. It will lead to his death.

Chapter Seven

"The Plot"

Camero: Boys, Cosmo is fuming. He's not sitting around doing nothing. He is in the cold blackness of "Tartarus" but he is laying his plans.

Henry: What does the word "Tartarus" mean?

Camero: From your world of the 21st century, that's the Hebrew word translated into your English as the word "hell."

Henry: Since Cosmo is in the blackness of outer space, then I see that the word "Tartarus" means the empty blackness of outer space! I also see why the word "Tartarus" means "hell," because that's what I felt like when we were trapped in the blackness of outer space with no hope before you came to help us. I'm sure he feels like that too.

Camero: That's right. But there is another word for "hell" which means "fire." That Greek word is "Gehenna." That is where Cosmo is finally headed. That will be his final reward. But he won't live forever there as many in your age falsely believed. The wages of sin is death, not eternal life in the fire. Once he has paid for what he has done, the fire will turn him and his followers to ashes. He will never exist again. He will be "annihilated" and cease to exist. He knows it. The fire is said to be "eternal" because no amount of water can put it out. It will burn forever until Cosmo and his rebel armies are ashes. Then, without anything left to feed on, the eternal fire will go out. The Great King is not going to have an eternal fire going on in his happy universe to spoil the perfect happiness of everyone. He is kind and fair. No one, including Cosmo will suffer one bit more than what they deserve.

But Cosmo is determined not to sit around and be bored. He knows that he is going to die, and he is determined to do as much damage as he can before he does. He has already been mocking the other messengers at the gates of the great city. The Great King knows that such determined rebellion will not remain inactive. Cosmo is now scheming up ways to try to hurt the Great King. But he especially wants to hurt his best friend - the Great Prince.

Even after the earth has been made, Cosmo spends part of his time just outside the gates of the great city - mocking the loyal messengers as they go in and out.

Knowing the power of Cosmo's giant brain, the Great Prince has instructed the loyal messengers not to speak to the arch-rebel when he comes near the gates. He cannot get into the city, but Cosmo tries to get the messengers who come in and out to debate with him. He laughs at them, and tries to make them think that he's having a great time.

Cosmo: Come over here you miserable morons. I want to talk with you minute. I'm having the time of my life! I didn't know how to live until I got free from this place. Now I have all the freedom I want. Come join me, and the rest of my brave messengers, and together, we can liberate the slaves in this city. We'll all be free and happy together.

Cosmo is cunning and as sly as a snake. He can make things appear just the opposite from the way they really are. He will soon use all his giant brain to dream up new and horrifying ways to hurt the Great Prince.

Meanwhile, He invites the messengers to join him in his new life of fun and games. {He doesn't tell them that he is really living in horrible misery, fear, and dread of his awful future}. Cosmo is the first great lobbyist.

Not only that, he is trying to invent some way that he can destroy the happiness of the first humans on earth. He will endeavor to fool and trick them into joining him in rebellion. He knows too well that this would cause grief in the city, and pain in the hearts of the Great King and his Prince, {whom Cosmo now hates without a cause}.

The arch rebel again goes off by himself contemplate the best way to pull it off. But soon, his followers are seeking him. He rouses himself, and, assuming a look of defiance, informs them of his plans to yank from the Great King the noble Adam and his beautiful wife. Cosmo conjures up the plan that if he can cast a spell on them, and in some way trick them into disobedience, the Great King will surely make some provision whereby Adam and his wife might be pardoned. Then Cosmo himself and all his fallen messengers would hopefully be able to share with them in this provision of mercy. Even if this should fail, they could unite with Adam and Eve; take possession of the earth, and hold it as their headquarters. And if they can gain access to the incredible "Tree of Life," their strength would be equal to that of the loyal messengers, and even the Great King Himself could not kick them out! So he thinks. Cosmo would then be the king of the earth, and the people who were made to one day sit on the throne with the Great King would become Cosmo's stooges. The earth would

become his empire!

Cosmo holds a consultation with his fellow rebels, but they don't all quickly agree to engage in this hazardous and terrible work.

Cosmo: Listen you lucky fools. We've got a big job ahead of us. I'm going to present to your tiny brains the fact that there is a chance that we can get out of Tartarus, and get us a nice place to live. Have you ever heard of planet earth? Hey hey!

I'm not going to trust this job to any of you lovely imbeciles. I'm going to handle it myself. Only I, the great Cosmo have sufficient wisdom and brains to pull it off. But I need you behind me. I need your cooperation. Yes, there's a terrible risk. But it's our only hope.

I want all of you to consider this matter carefully while I go off one more time to make my final decision, and lay my plans. I want you to understand that if we fail here, all hope of regaining and controlling the city of the Great King, or the earth, or any part of the universe is hopeless. **Hopeless** - do you understand!

COSMO now goes alone to mature his plans to hijack a planet. But he has no peace. He's not ignorant of the horrible risk he's taking. He fears that his purposes might be defeated. And even if he is successful in leading the happy couple to rebel against the Great King, should his plan somehow backfire, his own case will not be improved, but his guilt will only be greater, and his fate more dreadful.

LOOK at him. There he stands - the most powerful being ever made. His robe glitters with jewels, but it brings him no joy. He shudders at the thought of plunging the happy pair into the misery, guilt, and horror that he himself is enduring.

He is in a state of indecision. Now he's firm and determined. Now he's wavering.

His fellow messengers are seeking him - their leader, to tell him their decision. They will unite with him in his plans! They will share the consequences.

Cosmo sees them looking for him. He shakes off his feelings of weakness, and, as their leader, strengthens himself to brave out the matter. He tells them his plans.

Cosmo: Listen you sorry slaves. If I should come boldly upon the newly-weds and make complaints against the Great King and his son, they wouldn't listen to me for a minute. They would be ready for such an attack because our enemy is no doubt going to send His messengers to warn them against us.

On the other hand, if I seek to scare them with my power, I will accomplish nothing.

So listen now. Here's what we have to do . . .

Meanwhile Harry and Henry are ranging around the earth, flying to the tops of mountains, swooping down into valleys filled with myriads of flowers, and landing on snowy white beaches beside the lapping waves. They watch the noble Adam, and his beautiful wife - talk, work, and sport together. When the messengers from the city come near, the boys listen {unseen} to what they're talking about. They are delighted as they look at the many fabulous wonders - silver, gold, diamonds, red rubies, green emeralds, blue sapphires, and other gems, sparkling and glistening amid the grass and flowers. They laugh as they see the many animals and brightly colored birds and fish on this new, delightful planet - little knowing what horrors lie just ahead.

Chapter Eight

"The Terror"

Henry: I'm wondering Camero, will it get chilly at night? Since the man and woman have nothing on except that covering of light, will they get cold at night? What will they do to keep warm?

Camero: No, the happy pair do not get cold. It does not get cold on earth yet.

Henry: What do you mean "yet?"

Camero: Now, the earth is just as beautiful and happy as the other planet that I showed you. But there is a terrible danger lurking near. Soon, you will see that a horrible monster will threaten earth's first happy humans. If not averted, this horror will have an effect upon the temperature, the beauty of the earth, and upon the way earth people act.

Henry: That could only be Cosmo. He's the only monster I've seen anywhere.

Camero: We will do everything in our power so that this awful terror will be prevented. But for now, let's look around and see what we find.

The three range all around the earth, and they especially look at the glowing and glimmering garden where the first man and woman live. They see that the pair are extremely happy. With ethereal bodies, Harry, Henry, and Camero walk - unseen to the first humans, while gazing at trees covered with the most beautiful and scrumptious fruit. There they see vines growing upright, covered with giant grapes of various colors - larger than anything man will ever see again. In sky, field, lake, river, and garden, the earth can truly be called a "paradise."

Camero: Now listen boys. I'm going to show you something special.

The three travel to the center of the delectable garden, and come upon a magnificent and amazing tree.

Camero: Do you see that tree?

Harry: What is it?

Camero: It's called the "Tree of Life." The beauty of this tree surpasses all the other trees.

Henry: Wow! It's gorgeous! Why does its fruit look like apples of gold and silver?

Camero: This tree has special power. It has supernatural power. The Great King has given this tree the power to perpetuate immortality. The leaves contain healing properties.

Henry: Exactly what do you mean?

Camero: I mean that if you eat of that tree, you will live forever. You will never die.

Harry: Is that why the people on the other planets don't die? Do they have a tree like this?

Camero: That's exactly right Harry. They have the same kind of tree. Not only that, if you eat of the leaves of this tree, you will start growing up until you are the size of the lordly Adam and Eve.

Henry: Let me at it!

Camero: As you eat of those leaves, the DNA molecules in every cell of your body will be maintained in such a way that they will keep preserving themselves with no breakdown. The leaves of this tree have power to repair the cells of your body better than the most super anti-oxidant that your generation will know anything about. Not only that, with the fruit and leaves of that tree in your system, the cells of your body will not only live forever, but those leaves will keep you from even getting old!

Henry: Let me at it!

Camero: If you eat of that tree boys, you'll be young forever! Do you like that idea?

Henry: Wonderful! Let's eat it! Can we eat some now?

Camero: Not now.

Harry: You mean we can - some day?

Camero: If you meet the conditions.

Henry: Are they hard?

Camero: No. The Great king has made these conditions very easy and simple. His great heart is very kind, and He desires for everyone to be able to eat of that tree and live forever. As we move back to the future, you'll learn what those conditions are.

Harry: Great! I don't want to shrivel up and die. No one that I've ever known has escaped getting old and dying. This sounds too good to be true. It sounds like something the Great King would do - - to make the conditions easy!

Camero: Yes. The more you get to know him, the more you fall in love with Him.

Henry: Like you have?

Camero: Yes Henry. Like I have.

Henry: How dumb old Cosmo could have rebelled against someone so kind is still a mystery to me.

Camero: It will always remain a mystery to everyone. No one will ever understand it. In fact, it is called "The Mystery of Iniquity." There will never be a reason for it.

Harry: Will Adam and Eve get to talk with you messengers every day?

Camero: Yes. In fact, some of my fellow messengers have been talking with the happy couple already. We will come to them often and bring messages from the Great King.

Harry: What about the Great Prince? Will you bring messages from Him too?

Camero gets a certain look on his face which the boys wonder at. For a moment, he doesn't answer, but stands smiling. The boys notice a twinkle in his eye. Or is it a tear?

Camero: Boys, I'm happy to tell you that we will not always have to bring messages to King Adam and his bride from the Great Prince because our great and mighty Prince will get up off of His majestic golden throne - and bring personal messages to them Himself!

Henry: What a privilege!

Harry: Since Adam and Eve are the only people in the whole world, won't they ever get bored?

Camero: The joyful pair will never get bored because they are students, receiving instruction from the one who made the universe - the one who has all knowledge, and in whom is all joy. He will speak to them face to face. The mysteries of the visible universe will give them unending sources of instruction and delight. The sons and daughters of Adam and Eve will have pleasure for thousands of years in studying the laws and operations of nature. Adam and Eve are the first king and queen of the world.

Now we look back to the first day of Adam's life. It is also the sixth day of the first week of earth's existence. After naming the animals, and feeling a great desire for a companion, Adam feels a strange sleepiness come over him. The Great Prince secretly draws near and puts Adam to sleep. When he wakes up, there - before his astonished eyes - stands the most delightfully beautiful creature Adam has ever seen.

Adam: Who are you?

Eve: I don't know. I just woke up, and here I am. I was just now made by someone who told me that he is the Great Prince. He sent me over to you. He told me that He made you earlier today, and that you have already named the animals. He said that He waited to make me last so that as you saw that all the animals had mates and you did not, you would be even happier with me and would appreciate me more after you had been lonely.

Adam jumps up to greet her. His face is beaming all over.

Adam: You are so right! That's exactly how I feel. I want to get to know you. I'm delighted that he didn't forget me. What I mean is that after giving all the beautiful animals a mate, he didn't leave me out. He didn't leave me to be lonely in such a gorgeous place. Now, you and I can enjoy this wonderful world that we see around us, and together, sing praises to the Great King and his Prince for doing all this for us!

I gave the animals names earlier today. Now I will give you a name. Because you will be my wife, and the mother of all people on earth, I will call your name Eve.

Eve: Oh thank you! I'm only a few minutes old, but it seems like I've known you a long time. It seems like I belong here and that I belong to you. I enjoy being around you. I wonder how I learned how to talk to you. No one taught me how to talk.

Adam: There's no doubt that the same One who made you now, and made me earlier today taught both of us to speak the same language without having to learn.

It's now the sixth day after the earth was made. Before sunset, their wedding ceremony will be performed by the Great Prince himself. Though they are the only humans on earth, Adam knows that he'll never be lonely again.

Henry: Camero, I know that the Great King and his Prince were together when they spoke the world into existence. And I know that it was the Great Prince who did the speaking. But why was it that the Great King didn't make Adam or Eve, and why don't we see him here like we see his Prince?

Camero: After the world came into existence, the Great King went back to the city, and from now on, the Great Prince is his representative on the earth. From now on, whenever they do anything, or appear to anyone it will always be the Great Prince. The Great King will not be seen on planet earth until the great consummation.

Harry: The great consummation! What's that?

Camero: You're going to have to wait a while to know the meaning of this one. But I will tell you that it will be after the deadly work and plots of Cosmo are completely ended.

Henry: Oh great! I hope it won't be long.

Adam: Eve! Look at this!

Eve: What is it Adam? Why are you picking it up like that?

Adam: I have named it "Elephant." It's such a nice little animal with its floppy ears and long trunk. It's a chunky little thing. I'm about five feet taller than these elephants are, but - - ahhhhuuhhhaahh - - he's a heavy boy. They're so friendly!

Adam gently sets the eleven foot tall

elephant down, and it playfully gallops around him - shaking the ground with its massive body, and waving its trunk back and forth for more play.

Eve: Honey, you called it "little," but it's the largest animal I've seen.

Adam: You're right Darling. I'm just so happy with all the thousands of kinds of creatures that are playing around us that I feel playful myself. And I'm especially happy with you my sweet. Before you were made, I was happy in this lovely paradise, but all the animals couldn't satisfy the longing I had for companionship.

Eve: What about the messengers? They are not much taller than you are. I know that they have been coming to talk with you before I came. Was your desire for companionship satisfied with them?

Adam: No, my gorgeous doll.

He gives her a little squeeze.

Adam: Only you can satisfy my desire for oneness with someone like myself. Only you can share everything with me. Only you are like me - though you are more beautiful than I am. We are one. We are one in the same way that the Great Prince and his Father are one. I feel that I can open my heart to you, and share everything with you. Is that the way you feel about me - you lovely pomegranate?

Eve: Yes you handsome hunk of honey. And the visits from the Great Prince and his messengers increase our joy.

Adam: The Great Prince told me that he has made me the king of this planet. You are my queen. Together my sweet, we rule the entire world!

Eve. Yes love. The millions of beautiful animals have nothing to fear from us. We will only make them happy.

Look Adam. Look at these gorgeous pink and

yellow birds flitting around us.

Camero: Now here is something amazing for you boys to think about. The happy couple will actually be able to communicate with leaf and flower and tree, gathering from each the secrets of its life. In some way, which I will not explain now, the two can talk with even the vegetable kingdom, and the plants, flowers, and majestic trees will respond.

Henry: Wow.

Camero: With every living creature, from the mighty whale that plays in the ocean, to the insect mote that floats in the sunbeam, Adam will be familiar. As king, he has given names to everything on earth, and will be acquainted with the nature and habits of all. All the mysteries of science are opened to the study of earth's first parents. Adam's giant brain understands far more than the many scientists who will live in the 21st century from which you came.

As the three continue exploring the new world, they find that the most fascinating things on the planet are its king and queen. They watch the pair constantly discovering some attraction that fills their hearts with deeper love and gratitude to the Great King and His Prince. They watch them play. They hear them sing. Their songs of praise to the Great One who made them ring out on the air as the sun moves across the sky on the sixth day of the first week of earth's existence.

Their surroundings are perfect. Happy birds flit about their heads. The air is mild, comfortable, and is filled with music. The breeze is fresh and clean.

But from his haunt in the outer space blackness of hell {"Tartarus"}, Cosmo watches. The happiness of the perfect pair makes him all the more miserable, but there's a seething smirk on his face.

Chapter Nine

"The Danger"

Cosmo is not alone in his terrible plans. His army numbers hundreds of millions. They are restless. They are angry. Cosmo knows that he must turn their anger away from himself to someone else. All of a sudden, his seething smirk turns into a horrible grin.

Cosmo: Look at those lovely stooges down there. They're happy like we used to be. I'll fix that.

Camero: Boys, this is the first day of the life of Adam and Eve. They are both less than one day old, yet they are full grown. But this is the sixth day since the Great King and Prince started making the earth. When the sun sets in a few minutes, the seventh and last

163

day of the week will begin.

Henry: So what will happen on the seventh day? What will the Great Prince speak into existence tomorrow morning?

Camero: Nothing.

Harry: Nothing? Why not?

Camero: He will rest.

Henry: Is He tired?

Camero: No. The Great Leaders of the universe never get tired. They have never slept. They never will sleep. They have unlimited power which they constantly supply to every atom, electron, sun, star, blazing galaxy and system of the vast universe. If the Great King or Prince were ever to hold back their power for one second, everything in the universe would cease to exist. The very atoms would fall apart. The electrons would stop moving. Electricity would die out. Life would end. Everything would disappear.

Harry: Then how can He rest tomorrow?

Camero: It's like this boys. The Great King and Prince will rest in the sense that an artist who has just finished a lovely painting rests while sitting there looking at its splendor.

He will rest in the sense that a man rests in his love for the bride he has just married, and just sits there looking at her, admiring her beauty, and enjoying her presence.

Secondly, the Great King will set aside this last day of the week as a day for mankind to remember how the earth got here, for He well knows that Cosmo will try his hardest to get everyone on earth to forget.

If I know Cosmo, he will try to get men and women to think that the earth got here by accident, and that the Great King and His Prince do not even exist.

The Great King not only desires for man to rest with Him and enjoy what He has made, but on that day of rest, He wants men and women to get to know Him better - like two lovers who walk together - enjoying each other. Why? Remember boys that our beloved

King has plans for the people on this earth to one day be so close to Him that they will sit on thrones with Him, co-ruling the universe itself - like a queen with a King.

Harry: Wow. No wonder Cosmo was jealous! People on this earth are one day going to have a higher position than he ever had!

Camero: That's right. But before man can have that high position, he must be tested to make sure that he will never rebel like Cosmo did. We messengers have had our test and one third of us failed. Do you boys understand what's gong on, and why we all must be tested?

Henry: Yes. I think I can see that everyone in the universe must be tested to see if they are safe to be given responsibilities and privileges in their part of the universe without causing chaos and rebellion like Cosmo did.

Harry: But how are people on this new planet going to be tested?

Camero: That's where the terrible danger that

I mentioned comes in. I'm going to show you something that has the potential of bringing horrors and death to the earth. Follow me.

Camero now takes the boys to another spot in the delectable garden. Soon, they stand before a large and shining tree. It has glorious fruit that looks like bright red, curiously mixed with burnished gold.

Camero: Boys, look at that great tree in front of us.

Harry: It's almost as beautiful as the "Tree of Life."

Camero: The name of this tree is called the "Tree of the Knowledge of Good and Evil." You can also call it "The Testing Tree."

Henry: What does that mean?

Camero: This tree will bring the great test for Adam and Eve. If they pass this test, they will be prepared to sit on thrones one day with the Great King. If they fail it, they will be plunged into the same horrible condition that Cosmo and his fellow rebels are in. The Great King very much loves the people which will live on planet earth. As you know, they are the only ones in the universe that look like Him in their features. He loves them so much that He is giving them everything that unlimited power can give to make people happy. And since the stability of the government of the universe demands that all be tested, the Great King is making the test so easy, that if they are loyal, the test will be easily passed, and after the test is passed, they will be forever secure.

Henry: Does that mean that after they pass the test, the testing tree will be taken away, and they will never need to be tested like this again?

Camero: Even if the testing tree is never taken away, it won't matter, because after all the people on earth pass the test and are secure, the tree won't bother them, or even tempt them any more. At every resistance of the temptation to disobey, the temptation gets easier and easier to resist until it's not even a temptation any more.

Henry: Boy! I'd make sure I passed that test the first time! And what is the test?

Camero: The test is that the happy couple may eat of every tree in the entire world except this one. It's as simple as that.

Harry: That's it?

Camero: That's it.

Harry: Puff! That's the easiest test I've ever heard of! Anyone could pass that test. All you have to do is just stay away from it! Keep it out of sight! Not only that, Adam and Eve don't even need the fruit of that tree. They have so many millions of other trees to eat from that they aren't even hungry, and don't need that tree at all!

Camero: That's right Harry. It's the easiest test that can possibly be given. All Adam and Eve have to do is to stay away from that tree for a period of time, and the test will be over. Then they will be secure forever.

Adam and Eve don't know it, but Cosmo is watching every move they make. He is planning, hoping, scheming - how to trick them into eating of that beautiful, forbidden tree. But it won't be easy. They will be warned. They will know full well that the reward of staying away from that one tree is to be eternally secure and to one day be exalted to the throne of the universe. They also know that on the other hand, to eat of that tree means to be plunged into the same horrors that Cosmo is in, and finally - death forever.

Henry: As I look around, I can see that compared to this place, the palaces of Hollywood's movie stars are like the inside of a dumpster.

Camero: Yes. Unlimited control over everything has been given to the first humans. Just like in the great city and on the other planets, we see lions and lambs sporting together peacefully around them, or sleeping at their feet. Look boys. Now birds of every color are flitting among the trees and flowers - just above the heads of Adam and Eve. Their music is lovely isn't it? They are praising the Great King and His Son.

Henry: Yea! It's reminds me of the two magnificent flocks of birds doing the same thing on that other planet we visited. One flock was red and yellow. The other one was blue and yellow.

Harry: I liked the blue and yellow flock the best.

The first humans are charmed with the beauties of their home. They're delighted with the little songsters around them.

Harry: Listen! Adam and Eve are singing too. It's Beautiful!

Henry: I think Eve is singing alto.

Cosmo: Listen to those happy eggheads. I'll turn their songs of praise into curses. They may be praising my enemy now, but I will make them blaspheme his name. I will make them curse each other too. I will turn their heaven into hell.

Hey hey - bang your head.

Soon the fools will all be dead.

The Great King knows what Cosmo is planning, and sends messengers to warn the happy pair of the terrible danger.

Two messengers now speed on their way to visit them. The pair receive the shining ones from the courts of light with joyful innocence, expressing their grateful thanks to the Great King for surrounding them with such a profusion of beauty.

Adam and Eve tell them of their new discoveries in nature. They also have many questions to ask concerning things which they don't yet understand.

The messengers kindly give them the information they desire. They also tell them of the sad history of Cosmo's rebellion and fall. They

172

clearly inform them that the tree of knowledge was placed in the garden to be a pledge of their obedience and love to the Great King. They inform them that not only are they being tested on earth by this one tree, but that the people on all the other planets have had a similar test, and even the messengers themselves have all been tested.

The messengers tell the first couple that Cosmo and his followers totally failed their test by rebelling against the law and love of the Great King. The happy couple learn with amazement that the insane rebellion of this powerful messenger and his followers has plunged them into the most awful misery. Misery loves company. Adam and Eve are shocked to learn that Cosmo is planning to attack the earth and try to trick them into failing their test too - to be plunged into the same misery, doom, and approaching annihilation that Cosmo and his friends are facing.

The messengers tell the kingly Adam and his lovely bride that they can obey the law of the Great King and be inexpressibly happy, or disobey, lose their high estate, be plunged into hopeless despair, and finally die.

They tell Adam and Eve that the Great King does not compel anyone to obey, but that they always have a free choice. The great Ruler of the universe desires only a service of love, and love cannot be commanded. Only by love is love awakened.

Adam and Eve are told that Cosmo, the fallen foe is now the enemy of all who choose to be connected with the Great King and His dear Son.

Not only that, the messengers plainly tell them that Cosmo is planning to do them harm, and that it is necessary for them to be guarded, for they might come in contact with the fallen rebel at any time. Adam and his companion are told that Cosmo has become a monster, but that the arch-fiend cannot harm them while they yield obedience to the Great King, for if necessary, every messenger from the great city would come to their help.

The first couple are told that if they disobey the command of the Great King by eating of that one tree, then Cosmo will always be able to annoy, perplex, and trouble them, and that they must be under his fearful, terrifying power and must suffer the same penalty that Cosmo is facing.

With a tender look of compassion, the messengers caution Eve not to separate herself from her husband while she is working in the garden - for she might be brought in contact with the deadly enemy, and if they are separated from each other, they will be in greater danger than if they are both together. The messengers warn them to closely follow the instructions which the Great Prince has given them in reference to the tree of the knowledge of good and evil; for in perfect obedience they are safe. Then the fiendish monster can have no power over them. The Great King will not permit Cosmo to follow the happy couple with continual temptations. The monster can get to them only at the beautiful but deadly, forbidden tree.

Adam: Oh thank you! Thank you for telling us these things. I assure you that my dear wife and I will never be disloyal to our wonderful King. We wouldn't think of hurting Him who has done so much for us. We have tons of luscious food growing everywhere, and we don't even need the fruit of that tree. We will show our loyalty to our beloved King by staying away from it. It is our highest pleasure to do his bidding.

At this, the two messengers unite with Adam and Eve in the most beautiful songs.

Henry: That's gorgeous. Listen to that harmony!

Cosmo watches. His eyes are squinting at them. He hears everything.

Chapter Ten

"The Horror"

Cosmo: Listen to those bumbling idiots. I can't stand that singing any longer.

As the arch-fiend hears the songs of praise to the Great King and Prince, his envy and hate increase.

Cosmo: Alright you happy goons. Here I come - ready or not.

Immediately Cosmo changes himself into the form of a beautiful, sparkling, flying snake, and enters the garden.

Harry: Look Henry! That flying snake is streaking right into the garden! Look at it! It's flashing and sparkling as it zips through the air.

Camero: Listen boys. Now that the earth is in its infancy, the serpent is a beautiful creature with wings. As you can see, its appearance is bright, resembling shining, polished gold. It's the highest of all the animals, and can even eat fruit like man does. But I'm warning you boys that that is no ordinary serpent. It is Cosmo. He has come into the garden to begin his terrible work of destruction.

Henry: Oh no! I hope the happy pair don't fall for his deadly lies.

Cosmo takes his position in the tree of knowledge, and commences to leisurely eat of the forbidden fruit.

After some time, Eve – unconsciously at first – separates from her husband while she is working with the vines of the garden. When she becomes aware of this, she feels that there might be anger. But after thinking about it, she decides that she is secure because she has wisdom and strength to know if evil comes, and to meet it. This is what the messengers have warned her not to do.

Soon, Eve finds herself gazing with mingled curiosity and admiration upon the fruit of the forbidden tree. She sees that it is very lovely.

Eve: I wonder why the Great King has prohibited us from eating or touching the fruit of this tree? It looks so delicious.

Cosmo: Now's my chance!

All of a sudden, the monstrous fiend speaks to the lovely Eve from a branch of the tree. He flatters her beauty, and talks to her as though he can read her mind.

Cosmo: Hello you gorgeous doll. You're the most beautiful thing I've ever seen. Has the Great King told you that you can't eat of every tree in this garden?

Eve's curiosity is aroused. Instead of fleeing from the spot, she stays to hear a serpent talk. She knows that serpents cannot talk, but it doesn't occur to her that it might be the fallen enemy, using the serpent as a medium.

Eve: We can eat of the fruit of the trees of the garden, but we've been told that if we eat or touch the fruit of the tree that you are in, we will surely die.

Cosmo: You will **not** surely die! The Great King knows that in the very day that you eat of the fruit of this luscious tree, then your eyes will be opened, and you will be as gods, knowing both good and evil! Not only that, look at me! I'm eating this delicious fruit. I'm not dead am I? Furthermore, since eating of this tree, now I can talk! This tree gave me the power to talk! Just think of that! Someone is trying to keep something from you - don't you think?

Cosmo has been stuffing himself with the forbidden fruit, and he now picks another piece of it and gets ready to hold it out for Eve to take.

Cosmo: Look, you beautiful thing. If this magical fruit gave me power to talk, just think what it will do for you!

Cosmo is the first great crooked salesman. Eve is totally deceived. She is hypnotized. She is fooled. She is tricked. She has been caught off guard, and has no idea that this beautiful flying serpent - who is talking to her so lovingly, is the greatest monster the universe will ever see.

He gives Eve the idea that by eating of the forbidden tree, she will receive a new and higher kind of knowledge.

It is not the will of the Great King that the happy pair should ever know anything of evil, suffering, or death. He has freely given them the good and withheld the evil. Eve is thinking that the serpent must be very wise.

In his statement, Cosmo is calling the Great King a liar. He boldly insinuates to Eve that the Great King has deceived them by keeping knowledge from them which will make them equal with Himself.

The great deceiver has been biting big hunks out of the fruit, and he merrily tells Eve that the fruit is not only perfectly harmless, but is delicious and exhilarating. The monster tells her that he has received wonderful wisdom since eating it. The rebel leader also tells Eve that the Great King is so kind that nothing bad could possibly happen to her for eating fruit which has given him power to speak.

Cosmo hints to the wondering woman before him that the words of the Great King forbidding them to eat the fruit were just to scare them and keep them from great good. He further tells them that it is impossible for them to die.

Cosmo: Die? You? Impossible!! Has anyone ever died? There is no such thing! Have you not eaten of the tree of life? Of course! That means that you can never die! Hey hey!

Cosmo now holds out the fruit to Eve. What will she do? Does she remember that the Great King has given her and Adam everything to make them happy, and that if she passes this test, they will be exalted even above the high position which Cosmo had?

Does she remember that the Great King has given her everything, and that this snake in the tree has given her nothing? Does she consider that this serpent is now asking her to give her life and happiness, and everything - over to him - in exchange for misery and death? Does she remember that if she eats of this tree, she will be plunged into the same condition of approaching death and misery that Cosmo is now in? Or has she forgotten it all? What will she do?

Of all horrors. She forgets it all! Eve is entranced. In a state of curiosity and wonder, she takes the forbidden fruit from his hand.

Cosmo: Now look what you did! You're touching it babe! You're not dead now - are you? Hey hey! It was all a lie. You can eat this fruit all you want, and when you do - watch out - for you will rise higher and higher into a state of being that you never dreamed of!

Eve now gets more bold because she doesn't feel any immediate signs of the displeasure of the Great King.

She is thinking that the words of the beautiful serpent must be true. All of a sudden, Eve takes a bite of the fruit. The entire onlooking universe goes into shock. They know what Cosmo knows. They know that Eve must die. She doesn't know it, but powerful, shining messengers are weeping. The Great Prince, invisible, is nearby. His eyes are full of tears. His heart is breaking.

Eve is delighted with the fruit. It seems delicious, and she imagines that she is going into a higher state of being because of its magical powers.

She now plucks handfuls of it for herself and her husband. In a strange and unnatural excitement, she seeks Adam. With her hands filled with the forbidden fruit, she tells Adam about the wise and wonderful serpent.

Eve: Oh Adam, it's wonderful!

Adam: What? What is it darling?

Eve: Look Adam. This is the fruit from that wonderful tree where a very wise serpent spoke with me!

Adam: Spoke with you!

Eve: Yes Honey! Serpents can't talk. But this serpent is more powerful and wise than any animal on the earth because he was eating fruit from that special tree.

Adam: Was it the tree of the knowledge of good and evil?

Eve: Oh yes honey. And it's wonderful! Look! I ate it, and I feel great! Here Adam, have some! Together, we'll enter a higher state of being! If this fruit gave the wise serpent power to talk, just think what it will do for us! Here Adam, eat some with me! Come with me to the tree, and see the wise serpent for yourself. He will explain it all to you like he did for me!

A sadness comes over Adam's face. He looks afraid and astonished. A terrible struggle is going on inside of him.

Adam: Oh no Eve! No! I'm sure that this is

the enemy we've been warned against. He has tricked you Eve! If I'm right, then you must die! Do you realize that, my darling? You must die!

Eve: Oh Adam, don't be silly! I feel great! I feel wonderful. I don't feel any bad effects from this at all! Here - eat it with me Adam. Join me my dear husband! Let's do it together honey - and we'll reach for the stars!

Adam now understands that his companion has violated the only rule laid upon them as a test of their love. Eve reasons with her husband that the serpent said they would not die, and his words must be true - for she feels no signs of the displeasure of the Great King, but feels an invigorating influence that she imagines the wise serpent feels.

Adam: Oh Eve, Eve. My darling, why did you leave my side! Why did you allow yourself to be tricked into failing the only test that the Great King has given us! I regret this with all my heart. But, it's done now, and now I must be separated from you - my beloved!

Oh Eve, Eve! How can I bear to be separated from you my love, my dove? How can I bear to be alone, and have you die? I love you so much! What will I do? Oh what will I do!

Eve: Eat with me my darling! We won't be separated! I'm healthy and strong. I can't die. You can't die. The wise serpent said so! We've both eaten of the tree of life. Eat of this magical fruit with me Honey, and we'll live together - happy forever!

Adam's love for Eve is strong. In utter discouragement he decides to share her fate. He reasons that Eve is a part of himself; and if she must die, he would rather die with her than be without her. He can't bear the thought of separation. Adam doesn't stop to think that the Great King, who has made them both, can supply her place. He reasons that after all, might not the words of the wise serpent be true? Eve is before him, just as lovely and beautiful, and apparently as innocent, as before she ate the forbidden fruit. She is expressing greater love for him than before. He sees in her no signs of death. She is telling him of the wonderful influence of the fruit, and of her deep love for him. Adam decides to brave the consequences. He seizes the fruit from her hands, and quickly eats it!

Chapter Eleven

"The Plan"

From the planets of a hundred billion galaxies, the watching universe is filled with horror. They understand what this means. They know, as Adam and Eve cannot, that terrors and tortures are coming to earth from the insane, fiendish power of Cosmo - and that one day, they will die. Though not yet evident, Cosmo has succeeded in pulling the most highly exalted planet into the same condition of approaching doom as he is in.

The on-looking universe see that Eve has been tricked and fooled, but they know that Adam, as king and representative of the earth,

was not tricked. He purposely has failed the only test of loyalty that has been given, and he did it - knowing full well that it means death!

Henry: Oh no! I can't believe this! This is horrible! I feel worse about this than when Cosmo rebelled.

Camero: Eve thought herself capable of deciding between right and wrong. The flattering hope of entering a higher state of knowledge led her to think that the serpent was her special friend. But it was all a lie boys. All a lie! Cosmo hid from her who he was. He didn't tell her the horrible misery that he himself is feeling, and he didn't tell her that in failing the one test of love to the Great King, she was trading her great happiness and her very life in exchange for mental agony and future destruction.

Cosmo: Hey hey joyful day! I've come here now and here I'll stay. The lovers ate and now they'll pay. The dopes will die and all turn gray. We'll live on earth and all be gay. Hey hey you merry fools - joyful day!

Now Cosmo, and hundreds of millions of his rebel messengers come down from the blackness of space {"tartarus" = hell}, and in triumph, range around the beautiful earth - wilting the flowers and killing animals. They take possession of both the vegetable and animal kingdoms. The victorious rebel chief speaks to his army.

Cosmo: Will anyone object to us having a little fun on our own planet? King Adam just handed this world over to me you stooges! Do you realize that? Now I'm the king of this world! Hey hey! Is not this planet my rightful prize? Oh yes! He gave it to me when he obeyed me instead of the Great King. I own and control the life on planet earth now – and the Great Prince can't do a thing about it! He can't tell me not to warp or mutate my own animals! He can't tell me what to do with the flowers of my own kingdom - can he boys?

If I get a little revenge by torturing some of the animals to death, or if I make them eat each other, not even the Great King can stop me! By law, this world is mine!. Adam has chosen me as his master! Just think of that! Hey hey!

Listen now you delightful imbeciles. My plan is to bring such suffering on this planet as the noble Adam never dreamed of. As time goes by, I'll stay in the background so that his children won't even think that I exist. It's better that the people of earth don't believe that I'm around. Then the awful suffering that I bring to men and animals will be blamed on the Great King! Hey hey! I'll take control of the atmosphere. I'll bring things here that have never even existed in the universe. I'll bring hurricanes. I'll bring tornados and throw people out of their homes onto the streets. I'll bring earthquakes that will jiggle and wiggle these mortals and bring their roofs crashing down upon them - to scare the daylights out of them and wipe them out. I'll bring floods that will float these suckers down the stream to a watery grave. I'll roast and toast them in great forest fires - and their animals and flowers with them. I'll get them to fight each other, and torture each other, and then I'll make them think that the Great King is responsible for all this, and I'll make them curse Him!

Moroni: Cosmo, you're a genius!

Cosmo: Why of course, you mole head! But you haven't seen anything yet! Because this planet has been legally turned over to me by king Adam, we are protected here "by law." This world is now our headquarters! We made it you ant heads! Do you comprehend that? We finally made it! This planet will be the center of the greatest star wars the universe will ever see!

But there's more! Listen now – I've succeeded in capturing the natures of Adam and Eve, and turning them from their loyalty to the Great King - to loyalty to me! From here I will work to spread our empire to the other worlds. I'll turn the hearts of the people of the whole universe against the Great King. Then, we'll range from constellation to constellation. We will go from planet to planet - and all will obey me! You and I - my fellow morons - will co-rule the universe together! We will be the rightful kings of our own universal empire! Hey Hey!

At these words a great cry of hellish triumph goes up from millions of rebel messengers:

Cosmo: To pull all this off, I want all the universe to watch what goes on here. I will convince everyone on the planets of the entire universe that the law of the Great King is unjust and unfair. I will persuade them that it cannot be obeyed. I will offer them freedom from His law so that they will choose to obey me as Adam and Eve have done. I will make planet earth the theater of the universe!

I will trick and fool the fine citizens of the universe, and make them think that the Great King is like me, and that I'm like him! Hey hey! Then, they'll hate him, and they'll love me! Do you like this plan - you lovely pin heads?

As Cosmo has taken control of the natures of the first couple, he also takes control of the natures of the peaceful animal kingdom. He and his rebel messengers immediately start making the animals ferocious. Some of them start to kill and eat others. But that isn't all. With his giant brain, Cosmo starts working to mutate and cross-breed the peaceful animals that the Great King has made. These mutations will eventually become mammoth monsters. There will be giant dinosaurs, and ferocious, man-eating saber-toothed tigers and other killers. The eyes of Henry and Harry will be wide open in amazement as they later see what will become of these creatures.

Because of Adam's decision, Cosmo and his vast army of rebel messengers will now be able to follow earth people around and continually tempt and annoy them - harassing and killing both people and animals. As years go by, they will bring war, famine, floods, fires, disease, terror, and unimagined suffering to all forms of life on earth as they continually work to sink humans lower and lower. Cosmo well knows the plan of the Great King to exalt earth people above the position he had. So one day he will teach his slaves to spread one of his greatest lies - that people came from animals. This will be called "the theory of evolution," and will make people forget the Great King. This false theory will teach young people that they came from germs, worms, monkeys, and that people are just a higher form of animal - - while Cosmo is laughing at them, and is dragging their minds down toward the level of animals - from the high position that the Great King lovingly gave them. Cosmo is determined to twist their minds and drag them down until they're dead. Not only that, He will teach men to concoct chemical potions that will dull their brains and make them have no conscience. He already knows how to make alcohol, and he will teach people to use it so their brains will get so dull that they won't see clearly between right and wrong. Then, they'll commit crimes, have terrible accidents, kill each other - and blame much of it on the Great King.

After ranging around the planet for a while in triumph, Cosmo calls a meeting of his fellow rebels.

Cosmo: Listen now you mobsters. These eggheads will never sit on thrones with the great King. Adam might look like Him now, but our effort will be to constantly drag humans lower and lower.

Sit on thrones with the Great King? Ha! We'll haul them down. We'll shrink them. We'll get them to mate with animals. We'll have them living in caves. We'll turn them into pygmies. Adam used to be the king of this planet. Hey hey! No more! When he ate that lovely fruit, he turned this beautiful dump over to me! Now I'm king! Not even the Great King can get us out of here now!

Eve did a great job! Now these poor souls won't get anywhere near the throne of the Great King. They'll never see the city! They've chosen me as their master. Am I going to die? If I die, I'll take planet earth with me! We'll soon see what will happen in this great star wars!

Adam still has no idea of the magnitude of what he has done. And neither Cosmo, nor any of the messengers, nor the people of the other planets know the final outcome of Cosmo's terrible victory. They don't yet understand the final outcome of the great battle over the planet, but Cosmo well knows that he and his fellow rebels are now better off than they were in Tartarus - the boring blackness of outer space.

Cosmo has won the first battle in the war over planet earth. His attack has been a success. The entire universe now watches with intense interest to see what will happen to the first humans. Will they really die? How will it happen? Cosmo was cast out of the great city because of his rebellion. Now, like a horrible cancer, the revolt has spread to the beautiful new world. What will the end of these things be?

Camero: Boys, Cosmo promised the happy pair a higher state of wisdom and knowledge. But the only knowledge they'll receive from him is a knowledge of evil, a sense of guilt, misery, and approaching death.

All of a sudden, Adam and Eve are shocked. The beautiful covering of light that has surrounded them now disappears, and under a sense of guilt, they know that they are naked. A shivering seizes them. They now hide from each other, picking large leaves to try and cover their exposed forms.

How will they die? When will it happen? Is there any hope? Are they doomed forever?

Henry: Will the Great King somehow stop Cosmo's evil plot from ruining this planet? Will the horrible cancer of rebellion and suffering be allowed to go on forever as Cosmo hopes until the earth is totally destroyed? And will it spread to the other planets so that Cosmo and his rebel armies will control them too? Oh, this is terrible! Will the Great King somehow be able to stop Cosmo from pulling off more horrors and the death of millions?

Camero: This is indeed a terrible crisis for the world. I know that if Cosmo rules, the earth will finally be totally destroyed - for the seeds of death are in him. You will soon see the answers to your questions boys. But come now with me. I see that the Great Prince is approaching.

Harry: Eve believed Cosmo instead of the Great King. But what had the liar done for her?

Henry: Nothing. He took away from her every good thing and gave her approaching death.

Camero: The first couple chose to believe the words, as they thought, of a wise snake, yet he had given them no evidence of his love. He had done nothing for their happiness, while the Great King had given them everything.

After Adam eats the fruit, he imagines that he is rising into a new and higher existence. But soon the thought of his evil deed terrifies him. The air that had been of a mild and even temperature, now seems to chill them. The guilty pair have a sense of doing wrong. They feel a dread of the future - a sense of emptiness and nakedness inside.

The sweet love, peace, and happy, contented bliss, are gone. In place of these, are a dull fear of the future, and an empty, black hole.

To relieve the nakedness of their bodies, the unhappy pair now look around for something to cover themselves with. How can they meet the eye of the Great Prince and the shining, powerful messengers from the great city while naked?

Camero had taken the boys away before this happened. When he brings them back, they see the guilty pair clothed in fig leaves that they have sewn together for themselves.

Henry: Listen, I hear Adam and Eve talking to each other.

Adam starts scolding Eve's folly in leaving his side, and being deceived by the serpent. But they both flatter themselves that the Great King, who had given them everything to make them happy, might yet excuse their disobedience because of his great love for them. They are hoping that their punishment will not be so dreadful, after all.

Meanwhile, Cosmo, along with his vast army, is laughing and exulting in his success.

Harry: When earth's first couple failed their test, how did the messengers in the great city react?

Camero: Boys, they threw their crowns from their heads in sorrow. The whole city was in agitation. All my fellow messengers were grieved that the terrible and cruel Cosmo could have done this to them. And they were grieved at the ingratitude of the first man and woman to their loving King - in return for his rich gifts to them, and for the wonderful future promised them. A council was held to decide what must be done with the guilty pair. I know that many of the messengers have been fearing that Adam and his wife will now eat of the tree of life, and thus live forever in a state of rebellion. That's just what Cosmo wants! He wants them to live forever in misery and rebellion. That was part of his plot.

The Great Prince now comes to the earth to visit Adam and Eve. They do not realize what horrors the monstrous Cosmo is about to bring upon them, or the terrible extent of what they have done.

In love, sorrow, and pity, the kind Prince comes to reveal to the couple what will now happen because of their obedience to Cosmo instead of the Great King.

As the first couple hear the majestic approach of the Great Prince, they seek to hide themselves from His inspection. Just yesterday - in their innocence - they delighted, to meet with Him. Now his lovely voice frightens them. He hasn't changed. They have. The tender tones of His magnificent voice are heard in the beautiful garden, as, with pity, he gently calls to the frightened pair -

"Where are you?"

Henry: Did He call to them because He doesn't know where they are?

Camero: No. The Great Prince knows exactly where they are. He knows where everyone is at all times. He knows the position of every electron, neutrino, and sub-atomic particle in every planet, star, nebula, galaxy, and system in the universe. He guides them in their orbits. His awesome power and knowledge have no limit. He knows every thought that every person on every planet has ever thought or ever will think. But He gently calls to them because He is very tender. He knows that they are experiencing guilt, and He doesn't want to needlessly cause them greater pain or fear by coming upon them suddenly. He comes gently. He does everything as kindly as possible to lessen the suffering of all. Cosmo the murderer would cast them down. The Great Prince would seek to gently lift them up.

Harry: Oh, how kind and gentle He is!

From his hiding place among the bushes and lovely flowers, Adam answers.

Adam: I heard your voice in the garden, and I hid myself. I was afraid, because I was naked.

Great Prince: Who told you that you were naked?

Have you eaten of the tree that I commanded you not to eat from?

Camero: This question was asked not because the Great Prince needed the information, but to help the guilty pair to start realizing a little of what they have done. He is asking them why they have become ashamed and fearful. Just the day before, they were so happy. What caused this sad change in their close and loving relationship with Him?

Adam admits that he ate the forbidden fruit, not because he was sorry for his great disobedience, but he admits it to throw blame upon his wife, and upon the Great King for allowing his wife to tempt him.

Adam: The woman whom you gave me, she gave me the fruit of the tree, and I ate it.

Now the Great Prince turns from Adam and speaks to Eve.

Great Prince: What have you done?

Eve: The serpent tricked me, and I ate of the fruit.

Since the serpent was used by Cosmo as a medium to bring the horrible fall of the glorious new planet, the Great Prince now speaks to serpents everywhere - and through them, to Cosmo himself -

Great Prince: Because you have done this, you are now cursed more than any animal. From now on, you will crawl on your belly, and will eat dust.

The serpent had been exalted above all the animals - having wings to fly. As it flew through the air, it sparkled like polished gold. But from now on, it will be degraded beneath all animals. It will be hated and feared by both man and beast.

Turning back to Adam, the Great Prince speaks again.

Great Prince: Because you have listened to your wife, and have eaten of the tree that I commanded you not to eat of, the ground will be cursed for your own good. Cosmo has told you that he would give you happiness, but he will bring you sadness, and because you have chosen to obey him instead to the Great King who loves you, you will have to endure the rule of the rebel leader as you eat in sorrow what you have grown from the ground. Cosmo will cause thorns and thistles to spring up, and he will make it so that you won't have an easy time of just picking your food without much effort - as you have been doing. Your food will come to you through hard work and the sweat of your brow. You will eat it in this way until you return unto the ground. I made you from the dust of this beautiful new world which I have given you to rule over. Now, because of obeying Cosmo instead of the one who loves you, you will return to the dust of the very earth from which you were made.

Harry: Do I understand it right that the Great Prince is telling Adam that the ground is cursed because Cosmo has taken control of it - since Adam obeyed him as a master instead of the Great King?

Camero: That's right Harry. As time goes by, Adam and his wife will learn by hard experience the horrors connected with having obeyed Cosmo. Instead of the freedom and good life that the liar promised if they disobeyed the law of the Great King, they will learn that the rebel monster will make them slaves before he sees their dead bodies lying on the ground.

Boys, the universe is watching this horrible experiment in rebellion. They are going to learn that compared to the cruelty and torture that Cosmo gives his slaves - to follow and obey our loving King is supremely wonderful.

Cosmo is planning to get all the planets to believe his side of the story and follow him. Do you think that you can guess whom the planets will choose to follow?

Henry: It doesn't take me long to decide which one I want to follow and obey. That's for sure!

From this time forward, Cosmo and his rebel army will be able to follow humans around every day and tempt them to get worse and worse. Instead of the happy, cheerful labor he had enjoyed before his rebellion, Adam will now have a life of perpetual work and anxiety. Because of Cosmo's hateful rule, people on earth will be subject to disappointment, grief, sickness, pain, and finally death.

Cosmo was hoping that the guilty pair would stay in the garden and eat of the tree of life, so that they would be able to live forever as rebels against the government of the Great King. He had insinuated to them that the kind King was a liar, and that they would not surely die. Now, Cosmo wants them to quickly eat of the tree of life so that they can live forever in rebellion.

For this reason, Adam and his wife are informed that they will have to leave their lovely, glowing, garden home.

Adam: Please Sir, let us stay in this beautiful garden, I beg. It's our home, and we love it here! I know that we have given up our right to live here, but we won't obey Cosmo any more. We promise you, our dear Prince! We promise to be loyal to you and our King from now on.

The unhappy couple are informed that in their fall from innocence to guilt, they gained no strength but great weakness. They chose to obey Cosmo while they were in a state of happy innocence, and now they will have far less strength to resist him in a state of conscious guilt. They fell into rebellion when Cosmo could not contact them except at the forbidden tree. But now in their weakened condition, when Cosmo can follow them around and continually tempt them, they will have far less power to resist him than before. If they yielded to the temptation to eat from a tree which would bring them death, they would certainly cave in to Cosmo's temptations to eat from a tree which would bring them eternal life. Then, Cosmo's plot to bring everlasting misery to the earth and to all the universe would succeed.

Harry: Look at those two shining messengers streaking into the garden! What are they gonna do?

Camero: They have been commissioned to immediately guard the tree of life because Cosmo is studying how he can quickly get Adam and Eve to eat from it - and be eternal rebels. But these powerful messengers have been sent to guard the tree.

Notice boys that around these messengers are flashing beams of light which look like glittering swords.

Harry: Look at the faces of Adam and his wife! I see great sorrow written all over them as they are walking out of their garden home.

Camero: They understand better now why they can't stay there. They agree with their Prince, and see His wisdom in this great crisis.

Adam and his wife are starting to realize that the penalty of obeying Cosmo is death.

I'm going to leave you here for a little while as I go quickly up to the city. I want to learn a few more things so that I can tell you more clearly what is going on, and what is going to happen. Don't worry, Cosmo won't hurt you. In your present encrypted wave form, you are invisible to him. Neither he, nor the couple will hear you when you talk.

Henry: Well, here we are Harry. I feel so bad about what Cosmo has done to himself and is now doing to this world. I can't wait until we find out what's going to happen.

Harry: Me too. We're on such a beautiful planet - like the other one we saw - but it seems so strange to realize that a monster like Cosmo has taken control of it. It makes me shudder to think what he will do to the poor people here.

I wish all this hadn't happened. Now it's done. I hope Camero comes back soon. I'm anxious to know what he learned.

The boys watch the sad couple as they clear a space of ground to start growing crops. Before their rebellion, they didn't need to do much of anything to get food. They were in paradise, and spent their time joyfully training the beautiful vines to grow in any direction they pleased - making houses of living greenery and flowers. Now, they

must work and sweat to get their food.

After a while, Camero returns.

Camero: Boys, I'm back.

Harry: Oh good! What did you learn?

Camero: I saw that sorrow filled the great city as it was realized that the world which the Great King and Prince have made is to be filled with mortals doomed to misery, disease, and death - - and that there is no way of escape. The whole family of Adam must die.

Henry: Oh that's horrible!

Camero: I saw the lovely Prince, and noticed an expression of sympathy and sorrow upon his face. Soon I saw him approach the exceeding bright light which enshrouds the Great King. He came close to his Father, and they earnestly talked together. The anxiety of us messengers was intense while they were talking. After a while, the Great Prince came out of the intense light, but then went back in. Soon, he did it again. Three times I saw him shut in by the glorious, intense light about his Father, and the third time he came out, I could see his face. It was calm, free from all perplexity and trouble, and shone with a loveliness such as words cannot express. He then made known to us that a way of escape had been made for man. He told us that he had been pleading with his Father, and has offered to die in the place of man.

Harry: What!?

Camero: That's right. He offered to take the sentence of death upon himself, that through him, men and women might find pardon; that through the value and power of his blood, man can again have favor and be brought into the beautiful garden - to again eat of the fruit of the tree of life.

At first we could not rejoice. Our Prince told us everything. He held back nothing. He told us that he would stand between the death sentence of the law, and guilty man. He revealed to us that he will let that horrible death sentence fall upon himself. He told us that not many will receive him as their deliverer from disobedience and death, but nearly all would hate and reject him. He revealed to us that nearly the whole world will be tricked into siding with Cosmo, and accepting his lies against the Great King and himself. But He will leave all his glory in the great and shining city to make this amazing sacrifice of love for man - who will put him to death. He told us that in order for him to take the death penalty that man deserves, he would have to stoop down very low to humble himself, and turn himself into a man! Do you comprehend that boys?

Henry: Amazing! The Great Prince turn himself into one of us?

Camero: That's right Henry. As a human, our glorious Prince will become acquainted with the various temptations that people will have, that he might know how to help those whom Cosmo will tempt. As a human, our Prince will be able to teach earth people to resist Cosmo's temptations, and how to once more be loyal to the Great King.

Finally, I learned that after the mission of

the Great Prince on earth as a teacher will be accomplished, he will be delivered into the hands of men, and endure almost every cruelty and torture and suffering that Cosmo and his rebel army can inspire wicked men to heap upon him. Then, I learned that our kind and loving Prince will have to die the most horrible and painful death, hung up between the heavens and the earth - accounted as a guilty rebel - in man's place. I learned that he will suffer dreadful hours of agony, which even we messengers will not be able not look upon. His suffering will be so horrible that we will have to cover our faces from the dreadful sight. He will endure not merely agony of body, but mental agony so great that the suffering of his body will hardly be felt. The weight of the guilt of the whole world will be heaped upon him.

The Great Prince told us that he will die, and rise again the third day, and will then go back up through space to the great city, and come close to his Father to plead the merits of his own blood in behalf of the guilty people of this earth.

Harry: Amazing! When the Great Prince

told all the messengers these things, what happened then?

Camero: We fell on our faces. We couldn't stand the thought of someone so great and kind, and someone we love so much enduring suffering and torture greater than any human will ever endure.

Harry: Is the life of humans that valuable?

Camero: The love of the Great King for you makes you that valuable. He loved the world so much that He is giving His own son so that whoever trusts in him will not perish and cease to exist, but will live forever.

Henry: How did the messengers react to this after they got up off their faces?

Camero: Some of the messengers offered to give their lives to pay the penalty of death for guilty man - rather than to have our Great Prince suffer such horrors. But our Prince told us that the life of a messenger cannot pay the debt. He said that his life alone can be accepted by his Father as a payment for the rebellion of man.

Let me explain to you why it has to be this way. When man obeyed Cosmo, and disobeyed the law of the Great King, one of three things had to happen.

1) Man would have to die and never wake up.

2) The great law of the universe which man disobeyed would have to be done away with - abolished. Or -

3) Someone equal to that law would have to die in man's place.

The Great King loves man so much that he didn't want to choose option number one.

Henry: To do away with the law of the universe sounds like the easiest remedy. Could the Great King choose that option?

Camero: To do away with the law of the universe is just what Cosmo has been fighting for since he rebelled. Cosmo knows that if the law could be done away with, then there would be no right or wrong, and the chief rebel could get back into the Great City, because it is the law of life that keeps the murderer out. Cosmo knows that if the law of the universe could be done away with, then he could murder anyone, and lie, and steal, and do anything he pleases, and there would be no law to stop him. The whole universe would be filled with violence, and finally destroy itself. To choose that option would make Cosmo very happy. But the law of the Great King is the foundation of the universe. It is the standard of right and wrong. It is as sacred as the Great King himself, and can never be done away with. These are just a few of the reasons that option number two is totally impossible.

The only other option is option number three - and that is for someone equal with the great law of the universe to die in man's place. None of us messengers are equal to the law of the Great King. The only one equal with that law is the Great King, and the Great Prince. Many don't know it yet, including Cosmo, but the Great King and his Prince are equal - except that one has taken the position of a Father, and the other has taken the position of a Son.

Henry: Since they are both equal in power and knowledge, why did they take the positions of a father and a son?

Camero: It is so that all the people on the planets and we messengers can understand them better. It is so that they can relate to us better. You'll learn more about that later. One way that you can understand it for now is the way a child from your time relates to his loving and kind parents.

One of them would need to stay on his throne - guiding and upholding the vast universe. The Great Prince proposed to let his Father do this while he comes to earth to suffer and die in the place of man - to satisfy the claims of the broken law of the universe. Otherwise man would have to suffer the penalty of eternal death as his rightful reward for his own violation of that eternal law.

Harry: I bet the universe has never seen such love as this! I never have. Who would choose to die a horrible death in the place of someone who didn't even love him?

Camero: As time goes by Harry, you are going to see that what you just said is more true than you realize.

The Great Prince told us that because of his death, all men and women who accept him as their deliverer, and king, will not be condemned by the law any more, because the penalty of the law will fall on himself instead of them.

Harry: Amazing!

Camero: Not only that, because they will accept him as their ruler instead of Cosmo, the guilt of their rebellion will not only be washed away by his blood, but they will also be given strength to obey the law of the Great King. Then they will no longer be in slavery under the control of Cosmo - to be forced by him to keep breaking the great law of the universe. The Great Prince will give them power to obey it. In fact, he will write it in their hearts!

Henry: Wow! Then there's hope!

Camero: That's right boys. Because of this amazing sacrifice, all the damage that Cosmo did, will be reversed, and people of earth will again be able have the intimate and wonderful connection with the Great King, and will one day be able to sit on thrones with Him - as His bride - co-ruling the universe - just as if all the horrible work of Cosmo had never happened!

Harry: Whoopie! I feel like falling on my face myself - in thankfulness. What a wonderful King and Prince the universe has!

Camero: That's right boys. What he told us, helped us messengers to see that he has a beauty of character greater than we ever imagined. It makes me love him more than I ever did.

Henry: Wonderful!

Camero: After what our Prince told us, we could see why the life of one of us messengers could never be good enough to pay the debt of the broken law, or save planet earth from destruction.

But our Prince told us that even though our lives could not pay the debt for man, we would have a part to act in this great universal battle.

Harry: Battle indeed! This is the true star wars! What did he say that you messengers will do?

Camero: He told us that when he comes to earth as a man, his strength will not be even equal with ours. He said that we will have to help strengthen him. Cosmo will use his power to the utmost to try to trick our Prince into obeying him in some little thing. If he can do that, the Prince would be the slave of Cosmo forever, and the entire world would be destroyed by the horrible fiend. Our Prince will be walking on thin ice when he comes to this earth - because as a man, he will physically be far weaker than Cosmo.

The thought that Cosmo can drag the Great Prince down from his high position as supreme ruler of the universe with his Father - to suffer torture, and die a horrible death makes Cosmo happy. He has succeeded in causing great suffering to both of them.

Henry: When the Great Prince turns himself into a man and comes to the earth, will he still have supernatural power like a superman?

Camero: He will lay all his supernatural power down before he comes to the earth as a man. Everything he does will not be by his power, but by the power of his Father. Yes, he will do mighty miracles - even raising the dead to life, but everything will be done by his faith in his Father and by his Father's power.

Henry: Why?

Camero: He - as a human - must show the universe that men and women on the earth can obey the law of the Great King. Cosmo has been saying that the Great King is a liar {like himself} and claiming that it is not possible for men and women to obey the law of the Great King. Our Prince, as a man, must show the universe that Cosmo is lying, and that men, women, and children can obey the law of love - because he, as a weak human like you, is going to do it - and then write it in your hearts so that you can obey that law too!

Harry: Yippee!

Camero: The Great Prince also told us that when we see the horrible attacks that Cosmo will hurl against him, we will be stirred with the deepest emotions, and through our love for him, we will wish to deliver him from his awful sufferings and from his murderers. But he said that we must not interfere. We must not prevent anything we will see. He told us that he devised this plan to save man from eternal death, and that his Father has accepted it.

Henry: Wonderful! What else did he tell you?

Camero: The Great Prince knew that we were horrified at the thought of him turning himself into a human, and coming down here where this monster is - to be tortured and killed. So he comforted and cheered us up by telling us that because of his sacrifice, those who would accept him would be with him - happy forever - and that by his death he would receive the right to destroy him who had the power of death - Cosmo.

He told us that after it is all over, His Father would give back to him the entire universe, and he will rule over it in love - and the people from earth who accept him as their deliverer - will rule the universe with him. Cosmo and those who choose to follow him in his rebellion against the law of the universe will be destroyed, never more to disturb the great city, or any planet.

Our kind Prince told us to accept this plan that his Father has accepted, and rejoice that fallen man could be exalted again through his death, to obtain favor, and never die!

Harry: This is just great! It's just great! What happened then?

Camero: Then joy – inexpressible joy, filled the entire city! The messenger host sang a song of praise and adoration. We touched our harps and sang a note higher than we had done before - for the great mercy and love of the Great King in giving up his dearly beloved Son to die for a race of rebels. Praise was poured out for the self-denial and sacrifice of the Great Prince, that he would consent to leave the bosom of his Father, and choose a life of suffering and anguish, and die a horrible death to give his life for others.

Henry: Yes, yes. Oh yes! Was it easy for the Great King to accept the plan to let his Son die in our place? Did he make the decision without a struggle?

Camero: No, no. It was even a struggle with the Great King of the universe, whether or not to let guilty man perish, or to give his beloved Son to die for them.

Harry: I just thought about option number two again - about just doing away with the law. If that could be possible, then man wouldn't be guilty any more, and the Great Prince wouldn't have to suffer and die a horrible death in man's place - to pay the penalty of the broken law because there would be no law to be broken. Then there would be no guilt for doing anything.

Camero: I saw that it is totally impossible for the great law of the universe to be changed in any way to save lost, perishing man. The only options that could possibly be done were either to let the people of this planet die forever, or for the Great Prince to die in their place. There's no other way. To do away with the law of the universe was just what Cosmo wanted, but that is totally impossible because the law of the Great King regulates the orbit of every atom in the entire universe, as well as the lives of its inhabitants. It keeps order and peace, and love, and harmony. If it were abolished, the entire universe - and the Great King himself - must cease to exist. And that boys, is absolutely impossible!

But mark my words - Cosmo is so desperate that he has gone insane in his fight against the Great Prince and his Father. To trick people into fighting against the law of the Great King is one of Cosmo's main goals.

When this great battle is over, either Cosmo with his great army will be dead, or everyone on earth will be dead, and the Great Prince will be the slave of Cosmo forever. One or the other will happen. The life and destiny of planet earth depends on the success of the Great Prince against Cosmo when he comes to the earth as a weak man.

Henry: Oh boy. That makes me nervous. If Cosmo tricks the Prince into disobeying His Father's law in one little detail, it's all over!

Camero: Not only that Henry, but before this great battle is over, he is going to trick people into believing that the Great King has done away with his law! Do you comprehend that?

Henry: Oh no! How could the awful fiend

232

fool people into thinking such a horrible lie?

Camero: You will see, and you will be shocked when it happens. You will be horrified at who Cosmo will use as his puppets to fool billions of the people.

Cosmo has already learned that the Great Prince is going to turn himself into one of you, and come to earth and die in your place. Even now the fiend is laying his awful plans to destroy him.

Cosmo: Hey hey you happy goons! I rejoice, and leap up and down that by causing man's fall I can pull down my enemy from his high position! Listen now you boneheads. When the Prince turns himself into a mere human, I will be able to overpower him like I did Adam! I will trick him like I did Eve. I will hinder and stop the accomplishment of his horrid plan to save man from my power! All I have to do is to trick the weak human Prince into one tiny little violation of the law of the Great King, and his whole plan will be ruined! Hey Hey! Then both he and the earth will forever be in my power. I will rule the world forever! I will rule the Prince himself! He will be my slave. I will make him squirm. I will look down at his dead body!

Henry: He gives me the creeps.

Camero: I can see Cosmo as he used to be - a happy, obedient, powerful messenger. Now look at him! He still has a kingly form. He is still about 19 feet tall. But underneath that foolish mask he puts on, the expression of his face is full of anxiety, care, unhappiness, malice, hate, mischief, deceit, and every evil. Look at his forehead. It was once so noble. Now, just above his eyes, his forehead goes backward - like a dog or a pin-head. He has lost his forehead. He has lost the frontal lobe of his brain, which is right behind the forehead. This is the part of your brain where your conscience is. Now he has no conscience. Every good quality has been destroyed, and every evil trait has been developed. His eyes are cunning, sly, and show great penetration. His frame is large. But you see that the flesh hangs loosely about his hands and face. I saw him recently sitting in his haunt. His chin was resting upon his left hand. He appeared to be in deep thought. A smile was upon his face which made me tremble. It was so full of evil and slyness. This smile is the one he wears just before he makes sure of his victim. As he fastens the victim in his snare, this smile grows horrible.

Henry: Boy am I glad there is someone in the universe who has power to protect people from this monster!

I can feel that the atmosphere here on earth has changed. It's no longer perfect all the time. It's chilly.

Camero: The Great Prince has given Adam and Eve clothes made from animal skins to protect them from the chilliness of the night, and from the heat of the day.

Harry: Where did he get animal skins? There's no death here.

Camero: You'll see shortly.

Now the Great Prince commands

several messengers to speed to the sad couple to let them know that though they have lost their garden home, their case is not totally hopeless. They are informed that the Great Prince was moved with pity as he viewed their sad condition, and that he has volunteered to take upon himself the punishment due to them, and die - that humans on earth might live. They are told that all who accept his generous offer will be plucked from the death grip of Cosmo. The messengers reveal to them that all who put their trust in the Great Prince will be strengthened to resist Cosmo's power, and that through a life of trust in the death and life of the Prince for them, they will be delivered from guilt, and be strengthened to obey the law of the Great King instead of being the slave of Cosmo - doomed to share his fate.

Harry: Wonderful!

Henry: If a person rejects that wonderful

gift of life through the future death of the Great Prince for them, when will they die? Will it be right away, or when Cosmo dies.

Camero: You'll learn more about that later. But now that our kind Prince has offered to give his own life in place of people on the earth, there's no reason for anyone to have to die with Cosmo and his rebel messengers.

Henry: I understand the death that is coming to Cosmo will be a death from which he will never wake up. Is that right?

Camero: That's right Henry.

Harry: If someone chooses that death, they would be pretty stupid wouldn't they? Will there be many people like that?

Camero: I'm sure that no one would choose that kind of eternal death if they realized what they were doing.

Harry: What do you mean "if they realized?" Will Cosmo try to trick people into not realizing it? Will he somehow attack their brains so that they'll be so dull that they won't be able to appreciate this wonderful gift of life instead of death?

Camero: That's right Harry. I'm sad to say that the fiend will trick many into allowing their brains to be dragged down to such a low level that they will rather live for the pleasures of the moment that Cosmo will hold out to them, than to have everlasting life and joy forever with the Great King.

Henry: And how will Cosmo drag the brains of earthlings down to such a low level that they will be willing to have death instead of an unending life of joy?

Camero: One way Cosmo will drag their brains down is by their diet. He will work with evil men to produce foods and drinks that look, taste, and smell good, but will slowly dull the part of the brain that can appreciate the love of the Great Prince for earth people, and his gift of life through his death in their place. Now that the earth is so young, it won't be as bad as it will be in the century from which you came. Meanwhile, for several thousand years, there will be giants in the earth who are nearly as tall as Adam, and who will live to be almost a thousand years old!

Henry: Wow! Can the death of the Great Prince on the earth save Cosmo too? Will he also have another chance, and be on probation like man will?

Camero: I wish that were true Henry. But the death of the Great Prince will do Cosmo no good. As you know, Cosmo has already tried to kill him several times! When our kind Prince comes to earth it will be Cosmo himself who will inspire evil men to murder him.

The death of our Prince has power to save poor humans from eternal death, but will not help Cosmo because earth people - who are ignorant of the love and character of the Great King - have hope in learning of his love for them as they see the suffering and death of his Son in their place. His love can melt their hearts and win their love.

Cosmo, on the other hand already knows the love and character of our Great Leaders very well. He was very close to them - and in the face of all that love, he rebelled with fiery hate, and attacked our Prince in an attempt to murder him. You saw this with your own eyes. There is nothing more that our Great Leaders can do to show him their love. He knows it all. But his brain is totally set in rebellion. His heart is like stone. If he could, he would rip the Great Leaders from their throne of power, and would kill them both.

Through getting a glimpse of the love of the Great King for the earth, man has hope. But Cosmo chose to grind that tender love into the dirt. By his own stubborn choice, the case of Cosmo is now totally hopeless.

When Adam and Eve realized the horrible effect that their disobedience had in causing the death of their kind Prince, they begged to die. They said that they would rather die than to have their best Friend make this great sacrifice. The anguish of Adam was terrible as he saw that his wrong act was bringing fearful consequences. He couldn't stand the thought that his great Commander, who had walked and talked with him while he was innocent, must be brought down from his exalted position to suffer and die because of his own wicked act.

But he was told that this was the only way. And he was comforted with the thought that after it is all over, everything will be alright, and all who choose a life of trust and obedience instead of rebellion with Cosmo, will be happy forever.

Harry: How will the people of earth learn about this great sacrifice of our Prince? Will messengers come down to each one as the years go by?

Camero: I'll tell you. While I was taking you on a guided tour to other parts of the world, the

Great Prince himself came to Adam and asked him to do something that seemed very strange. He told him to go and get a little innocent lamb and bring it.

Henry: When Adam brought the lamb, what happened?

Camero: The Great Prince told Adam that he wanted him to kill it.

Henry: Oh no! I didn't think that the Great Prince wanted to hurt or kill anything!

Camero: He doesn't.

Henry: Then why . . . ?

Camero: Adam was told that this innocent little lamb represented the Great Prince himself - who will come to earth one day and die in the place of guilty man. So every time a person disobeyed the law of the Great King, and came under the penalty of death, he could come to where he worshiped the Great King, and bring a lamb and kill it - showing that he had faith in the coming Prince - who was innocent - and would die just like the lamb - to pay the terrible penalty of his sins. This painful ceremony will help the people of earth to not forget that the kind Prince is coming one day to do this for them - {for Cosmo will work hard to get people to forget it.}

Not only that, but Cosmo will one day pervert this ceremony so that after he gets people to forget that the killing of the lamb represents the death of the Prince of the Universe to save people from death, the monster will trick people into offering their own children on alters to various gods. That's right! He will trick them into killing their own children!

And not only that - but one day, Cosmo will trick people into worshiping him, and get them to offer goats on an alter to him - as a counterfeit of the ceremony set up by the Great King - to point people to the death of His Son in their place. Then Cosmo will laugh and mock at the Great Prince, and tell him that people also are offering goats when they worship him!

Harry: For Adam and Eve, who have never

seen death or suffering of any kind, this ceremony seems like it would be a terrible ordeal.

Camero: Yes, it will be. But this terrible ordeal of killing an innocent lamb will also help people to see what a horrible thing disobedience to the law of love is - causing the death of the Great Prince, and causing the death of anyone who doesn't receive this free gift of life through His death for them. It would help him to be very careful not to disobey the law of the Great King any more. Disobedience to the eternal law of the Great King is more terrible than people think.

Henry: So how did Adam feel about the first time he had to kill a lamb?

Camero: As he killed the innocent victim, he trembled at the thought that his evil deeds must shed the blood of his beloved Prince - the spotless "Lamb." The great sixteen foot giant stood there trembling in horror. He cried like a baby. And he marveled at the great love that would give such a ransom to save the guilty people of earth. A star of hope illumined the dark and terrible future and relieved it of its total desolation.

Not only that, the Great Prince revealed to Adam some of the future in order to encourage him. He saw important events that would happen on earth after his death.

Harry: Can we see them too?

Camero: Yes. You will see many of them on your way back to the time on earth from which you came. You will see awesome things. You will see things that will make you tremble. You will see things that will make you laugh. You will see things that will make you weep. You will see things that will make you shout.

Henry: What things?

Camero: Hold on my friends. Here we go.

Chapter Twelve

"The Problem"

As Camero guides the cousins down through the years, they see the first baby born on the earth. Eve is excited. She thinks it might be the promised deliverer who will save them from Cosmo's insane power, and from eternal death. She names him Cain.

With tears, the cousins watch Adam staggering under the great tide of evil {which everyone blames him for.} The boys see Cosmo overspreading the world with horrors. They see the monster and his dark armies hurl suffering, disease, sadness and death upon man and beast.

With amazement, the boys watch great armies of messengers fighting in the air. Armies from the city of light are fighting to hold back Cosmo's fiendish troops from murdering all the animals, the beautiful birds, and the people.

Harry: Look! Adam is bringing his sons and daughters to the gate of the garden. Does he think he'll get past those tall messengers guarding the gates with their flaming swords?

Camero: No Harry. Adam and his family are renewing their vows of obedience to the Great King, and to the law of the universe. They're grateful that their King is protecting them from being murdered by Cosmo and his angry mob of rebel messengers. Look at him there. He's bowing in thankfulness that a way of escape from eternal death is being provided by the future death of the

Great Prince for the human family.

As many years go by and people multiply on the earth, the boys watch with squinty eyes as Cosmo and his invisible rebel army laugh and leap up and down as they lead evil men to hurt and murder those weaker than themselves. They see people becoming bloodthirsty, as for the first time they kill animals for pleasure, and then eat the muscles and fat - filled with blood, right off of their bones!

But before so many people spread around the land, things are more peaceful as the cousins watch Cain and his younger brother {Abel} grow up. Adam's life is a sad one as everyone seems to blame him for every bad thing that Cosmo is doing. But he has some happiness as he and his wife raise the first two boys on earth. They love to play with the little ones. They love to watch them play with the animals and with each other.

Camero: Boys, I want to tell you about Cain and his brother. They're just little boys now, and it's wonderful that they're bringing joy to their parents - who have had so much sorrow as a result of what they did. All the trillions of planets are watching the joy of their little family.

Harry: You mean the people on all those planets are able to watch everyone on earth? Right now?

Camero: Right now. The Great King has made planet earth to be the theater of the universe.

Henry: Why?

Camero: Because this great experiment of rebellion and of the deliverance provided by the future death of the Great Prince in man's place, will be an eternal safeguard - to keep all the other planets from falling into the same trap of disobedience that Adam and Eve fell into. As time goes by, all the worlds will see the horrible anger of Cosmo - in his hellish efforts to ruin and destroy the people of earth. It will make the entire universe cling in loyalty to the Great King and his Prince. They will see how wonderful it is to obey the great law of love - allowing them to live forever in joy and peace, instead of being a slave to Cosmo and ending up with him - dead forever.

Harry: Wow.

As the boys travel down through the years, they see that Cain and Abel are greatly different in character. Abel has a spirit of loyalty to the Great King. He sees the justice and mercy in the Creator's dealings with the fallen race, and he gratefully accepts the hope of being delivered from Cosmo's power. But Cain cherishes feelings of rebellion, and murmurs against the Great King because of the curse pronounced upon the earth and upon man for his father's disobedience. He permits his mind to run in the same channel that led to Cosmo's fall--indulging the desire to build up himself in the eyes of others, and questioning the justice and authority of the great Leader of the universe.

Camero: The brothers are going to be tested like us messengers, and like their parents were. They don't know it, but they will prove to the universe whether or not they will believe and obey the word of the Great King.

Cain and his brother know that the Great Prince instructed Adam to bring a lamb and offer it as a sacrifice after they had disobeyed. They know that it represents the death of the Great Prince in man's place when he comes to earth in the future.

The boys watch as both Cain and Abel set up their altars alike. The brothers don't know that the entire universe is watching them. If they did, how differently they would feel!

The cousins see that the brothers each bring an offering. Abel presents to the Great King a sacrifice from his flock of sheep in

251

accordance with the directions which the Great Prince has given. All of a sudden - Crack!

Henry: Wow! Look Harry! A blinding flash of fire falls from the sky like lightning and burns up the lamb that Abel put on the alter!

Harry: I think I see the meaning in this. I see that just like the Great King sends fire and burns up the lamb, so, in the future, the Great King is somehow going to have a part in the death of his own beloved Prince - as he suffers the death that man deserves. Is that right Camero?

Camero: That's exactly right Harry. That's why the Great Prince has instructed Adam and his children to bring a lamb as a sacrifice instead of an apple or a tomato. The broken law demands the death of the one who breaks it. And the only thing that can take the place of man's death is the death of the Great Prince. Since the death of the lamb on that alter represents the death of the

Great Prince, that is why Abel brings an innocent little lamb instead of something else.

Henry and Harry watch with wide eyes as they see Cain now bringing tomatoes, corn, and other vegetables to present to the Great king on his alter. Nothing happens.

Cain: Send fire please.

Nothing happens. Cain waits.

Cain: Send fire Great King. Please.

Nothing happens.

Cain: What's wrong? What's wrong! Send fire Great King!

Nothing happens.

Cain: I'm so angry - #@%^%&%^&*@%#*.

Abel is watching painfully. **Finally he comes up to his brother. Cain's face is all screwed up with anger.**

Abel: Please Cain. Please don't come before the Great King with stuff from your garden. Why should you be angry at him? It's not his fault that he's not sending fire to burn up your offering. Fruit and vegetables aren't what he told us to bring. They don't represent the death of the Great Prince in our place. The lamb does. To bring a lamb shows that we are meeting the condition of the promise to deliver us from death forever, and from the power of Cosmo. By bringing vegetables, you're mocking the great King. Why should you be angry that no fire falls to burn up a pile of tomatoes and pears when you didn't meet the condition of the promise?

Cain: You bozo. You're younger than me and here you are instructing me like I'm your baby. I'm going to bring whatever I want to bring. It's the best I've got. The Great King should accept it.

Abel: It's no problem my brother. I'll give you a lamb to bring.

Cain: I don't want your old lamb. If the Great King isn't happy with my fruit and vegetables, then that's tough.

Abel pleads with his brother to approach the Great King in the way that He had instructed. But his pleas only make Cain more determined to keep on with his disobedience. As the oldest, he feels that his younger brother shouldn't bother him with his advise.

But not only that - Cain comes before the Great King with murmuring and unbelief in regard to the promised sacrifice. His gift expresses no sorrow for sin. He feels that it would show weakness to follow the exact plan marked out. He thinks it would show weakness to trust completely to the sacrifice of the promised Saviour to come. He will come in his own merits. He presents his offering as a favor done to the King, through which he expects to secure his approval.

Camero: Boys, Cain is wrapped up in himself. Even his offering is selfish. Why?

Because he doesn't bring what's required. Here's a lesson for everyone. Cain is giving only a partial obedience. He left out the part that shows his need for the Deliverer.

Now I will tell you what will happen in the future. Down in your day in the 21st century, people will do the same as Cain is doing now. They will claim to serve the Great King and to be on his side, but they will secretly be on the side of Cosmo.

Henry: Oh no!

Camero: That's right. They will go to places of worship, but many of them will not obey the Great King. Cosmo will have them as his secret slaves. They will be on his side in this great universal battle while outwardly saying that they are on the side of the Great King and his Prince.

Henry: That's tricky!

Camero: Yes. They will be Cosmo's greatest secret agents.

Harry: What harm can they do?

Camero: Others who go to worship the Great King and his Prince will see how careless and disrespectful these supposed worshipers are, and they will

tend to become like them. As they see the disobedience and carelessness of these professed followers of the Great King, they will think that it must be alright for them to be disobedient too. Cosmo will laugh at them. His invisible armies will laugh at them. They will mock the Great Prince with words like -

"These are your followers! Hey hey! They obey me! Their phony words praise you in their wacko meetings, but they obey me when they go home! They are my best workers! They are leading your followers to become like them. They don't know it, but they are like me! I couldn't do a better job myself! Hey hey! I use them to get more and more of your stooges to become careless and to not perfectly obey you, but to obey me while fooling themselves and thinking that they are on your side! Nobody has the power to turn your followers into my followers as much as these people who go to meetings to worship you! And your ignorant people don't even know what's going on! Hey hey, happy day, all the fools will soon be grey."**

Henry: I'm in shock. This is so tricky I can't believe it. Who will be able to escape this horrible thing?

Camero: People like faithful Abel will escape. Abel grasped the great principles of the deliverance from Cosmo's power. He saw himself as a breaker of the great law of the universe, and he saw that the penalty is death. He was not like Cain. Abel was obedient to the Great King, and he offered the killed lamb on his alter - showing that he accepted the love of the Great King in giving his beloved son to die in his place - as the lamb represented. Through the symbol of the shed blood of the little lamb, Abel is looking to the future sacrifice of the Great Prince dying on a wooden cross for the people of the earth. The reason that Abel's offering was accepted, and that fire came down and burned it up, was because his offering to the Great King was an offering of obedience and faith. Cain's offering was an offering of disobedience and unbelief. He did what Cosmo wanted him to do. In the end boys, there will just be these two groups in the world. Just two.

Harry: Now I can see why Cosmo sends his rebellious group to the meetings where people worship the Great King. They'll be infiltrators whom Cosmo will use to get many good people to switch and become secret rebels against the government of the King - while pretending to serve him. No wonder Cosmo will laugh!

Henry: That's not fair!

When Cain saw that his offering was rejected, he was angry with the Great King and with Abel. He was angry that the King did not accept his fruit and vegctables, in place of the lamb. And he was angry with his brother for choosing to obey the Great King instead of joining in rebellion against Him.

Even though Cain ignored the divine command, the merciful King did not leave him to himself. He sent a special messenger from the city to reason with this man who had shown himself so unreasonable.

Messenger: Why are you angry Cain? If you do well, won't you be accepted? But if you won't follow the plain instructions of our kind and loving King, how can he give you approval?

Cain: Aw, go away.

Instead of acknowledging his rebellion, Cain continued to complain about what he called the injustice of the Great King, and to cherish jealousy and hatred of Abel. He angrily slurred his brother, and attempted to draw him into an argument concerning the dealings of the Great King with them. In meekness, yet firmly, Abel defended the justice and goodness of their great

Leader. He pointed out Cain's error, and tried to convince him that the wrong was in himself. He pointed to the King's compassion in sparing the life of their parents when he might have punished them with instant death.

Abel: The Great King loves us Cain. If he didn't, he wouldn't have given us his innocent Son to suffer the penalty which we deserve.

All this caused Cain's anger to burn the hotter. Reason and conscience told him that Abel was right; but he was enraged that one who had always followed his counsel should now presume to disagree with him.

Camero: Boys, Cain wants Abel to sympathize with him in his rebellion. Abel won't do it. I see a terrible danger. Cain has hate in his heart. I can see that he is in the same position that Cosmo was in when he rebelled in the Great City. Look at Cain's face boys.

Henry: I see the hate too. Please Cain! Please calm down!

I wish Abel would get away from him. By the look on Cain's face, it's too dangerous to argue with him now.

Get away Abel! Go away from Cain!

Can you hear me?!

Camero: I'm sorry Henry. Remember that you are like a computer read-only file. No one on the earth can see or hear you. Your body is still in an ethereal form - similar to when you were sent into the far reaches of space from what you called "that terrible time machine." Then, you were in the alpha one mode. Now, I have put you into alpha two, to get you out of the time warp you were in, and off the path you were on - but until you get back to the 21st century, you can watch, but you cannot affect anything or anyone. As far as they are concerned, you do not exist.

Harry: Oh I wish we could do something to help the situation! What about you Camero! You aren't trapped in time like we are. Can't you appear to Cain and Abel and plead with them? Can't you warn Cain to calm down, and warn Abel to get away from his brother for a while?

Camero: I wish I could Harry. But the Great Prince has instructed us messengers that we must not interfere with the decisions of humans on earth unless there is some emergency in which he tells us just what to do. As I told you when we first met, sometimes the Great Prince does have some of us to appear to men in their own form and do something to save them from Cosmo's insane anger and power. But he will never have us to interfere with man's free choice. Men and women are to be tested on the earth to see which of the two powers they will obey, and to see who will be worthy to sit on thrones with the Great King in the future - to co-rule the universe according to his original plain. So people must be allowed to show whether they will be obedient or disobedient. They must pass the test that Cosmo and his fellow messengers failed. The failure of the first two humans was different than the rebellion of Cosmo. They were tricked and fooled by him, but Cosmo had no one to tempt or trick him. Rebellion originated with him. He rebelled against the amazing love and kindness of the Great King in the full light of the peace and joy of the Great city.

Henry: Uh oh! Look what's happening!

AS Cain and Abel continue to talk, Cain gets more and more angry.

Cain: You bad baggonzo! You dare to correct me! I'm older than you are. You have always obeyed me. Now you're telling me what to do! I'm going to fix you so you'll never tell me what to do again!

In the fury of his passion Cain leaps on Abel and kills him.

Henry: Oh no! This is horrible! Now look at him! There's Abel's blood running all over the ground. It looks like Cain is digging a hole under that flowering bush.

Harry: He's strong! He's digging fast with his bare hands!

After hiding Abel's body, Cain runs away. By this time, Cain and Abel have many brothers and sisters, and Cain doesn't want any of them to find the bloody body of Abel.

Camero: Look at Cain laughing boys. He thinks that no one will ever find Abel's body, and that now he will be free from Abel's words of correction.

Cain doesn't know it, but someone beside us saw him kill his brother. "Be sure your sins will find you out." It won't be long until he will have to answer for what he did.

Cain hated and killed his brother, not for any wrong that Abel had done, but because his own works were evil, and his brother's were good. So in all ages of the earth, the wicked will hate those who are better than themselves.

Cain was moved by the spirit of Cosmo. And whenever there are any who will stand in favor of the loving law of the Great King, Cosmo will move upon his slaves to attack them.

All of a sudden, Cain is surprised by a great voice behind him.

Great Prince: Cain. Where is Abel your brother?

Cain: I don't know. Am I my brother's keeper?

Camero: Boys, Cain has gone so far in rebellion that he has lost a sense of the continual presence of the Great King, and that nothing can ever be hid from him. Now he is telling lies even to the Great Prince in order to try to hide his guilt.

Great Prince: What have you done? The voice of your brother's blood cries to me from the ground.

The great and kind Prince gives Cain an opportunity to confess his horrible crime. This is the first murder of a human life the universe has ever seen. Cain knows a little of how guilty he is for this horrible crime, but he is rebellious still.

The judgement against Cain is executed immediately. The tender voice of the Great Prince - which has been heard pleading with the rebellious one, now pronounces the terrible words:

"Now Cain, you are cursed from the earth, which has opened her mouth to receive your brother's blood from your hand. When you cultivate the ground, it shall not yield to you her strength. A fugitive and a vagabond shall you be in the earth."

Harry: Why didn't the Great Prince kill Cain? Didn't he deserve it? And won't the death of Cain prevent him from being used by Cosmo to corrupt many others on the earth?

Camero: That's a good question Harry. It would seem that you are right. But there's more to it. The Great Prince didn't kill Cain for the same reason that he and the Great King didn't kill Cosmo. Do you remember why that was?

265

Harry: Oh yes! I forgot. I should have remembered. It was because if he had killed him right away, then everyone in the universe would have served him from fear instead of from love. I see now that in order to help people serve our Great Leader from love and not fear, they have to let evil play itself out and show itself for the horrible thing it is. People on earth, and on the other planets have to see how awful disobedience to the great law of love really is. Then when evil men and evil messengers finally get the endless death that they have earned, no one in the universe will blame the Great King for being unfair, but will praise him for both his mercy and for his justice.

Camero: That's right Harry. And even they themselves would choose eternal death rather than to live forever in the presence of the pure and happy beings in the Great City.

Harry: I'm seeing more and more what a wonderful and kind Leader the Great King is. It makes me love him.

Camero: You are learning a little of why we loyal messengers - who weren't tricked by Cosmo's lies - love to bow before him, and sing his praises. And now we are praising our Great Prince for offering to come to this earth one day and give up his life for a race of rebels.

Henry: I don't understand such love.

Camero: Neither do I Henry. It's a love that loves the unlovely.

Another reason that the Great Prince is sparing the life of Cain from instant death is to give him an opportunity to be sorry for what he has done. Our great Leader is so kind that even now - after Cain has committed this horrible murder of his own brother - if he will become truly sorry for what he did, the Great King will forgive him on the basis that his Son is going to die in his place and suffer the penalty for what he did.

Harry: Wow!

But Cain does not let himself become sorry for what he had done. He lives only to harden his heart, to encourage rebellion against the authority of the Great King, and to become the head of a line of bold, reckless rebels.

As Henry and Harry go through the years on their way back to the 21st Century, they see that this one rebel - Cain - led on by Cosmo, becomes a tempter to others; and his example and influence exert their corrupting power, until the earth becomes so corrupt and filled with violence as to

call for its destruction.

Cosmo: Look, you happy goons. Our work of corrupting the earth is right on schedule! Hey hey! I'm glad that Cain's life was spared because I'll use him to help make millions more just like him. I'll fill the whole world with beautiful people like him.

Riptera: Why do you call Cain beautiful great leader?

Cosmo: Because he's like me you bean head. I can't wait until everyone is like Cain. No doubt the Prince will spare their lives too. When there'll be more of them than the number of stooges like Abel, then I'll rule this world according to my will. Hey hey! Don't worry you toad stools. It's just a matter of time. I'll win in this great star wars. The universe will be mine! You just wait and see!

Harry: He gives me the creeps. I wish he'd go into outer space and never come back. The universe will be so glad when he has ceased to exist!

Camero: Listen now boys. Here's a lesson for you. In sparing the life of the first murderer, the Great King presented before the whole universe a great lesson. The dark history of Cain and his children will be an illustration of what would have been the result of permitting disobedient people to live on forever to carry out rebellion against the King of the universe. Even in view of his tender mercy, you have seen the people of earth becoming more bold and defiant in their rebellion against him and against his law of love.

Cosmo is constantly at work, with intense energy and under a thousand disguises, to misrepresent the character and government of our King. With vast, well-organized plans and marvelous power, he is working to hold the inhabitants of the world under his deceptions.

Our King has all power and is all-wise. He sees the end from the beginning, and in dealing with evil, his plans are far-reaching. It is His purpose, not merely to put down the rebellion, but to demonstrate to all the universe its nature. That way, people can choose to follow him into life and peace and joy forever, or to follow rebellion and be plunged with Cosmo into the eternal death that he is headed for.

Henry: Awesome!

Camero: When we first met, and you were asking so many questions, I seemed to put you off for a while - saying that you would learn many things in their proper time. I know it was hard for you to wait, but now, it seems that answers to many of your questions about the Great King and what he is like, are flying at you from every direction.

Harry: You can say that again! I'm amazed. We're learning about the character of the Leaders of the universe from how they've been dealing with Cosmo, with Adam and Eve, and now with Cain. And we've also been learning about what Cosmo is really like. He's a lot worse than I thought. But what about all the many thousands of other people who have been born and are spreading around the world?

Camero: There's one thing that you can always be sure of.

Henry: What's that?

Camero: It's that the Great King and his Prince never change. They are always the same. But keep in mind that there is a limit - when mercy ceases her pleading and justice takes over. You see boys, it takes both justice and mercy to make love. Cosmo is trying to tear the two of them apart. But they must always be together.

Harry: I don't think I understand that.

Camero: I didn't think you would. But the day is coming when you will. When the Great Prince comes to the earth in human form and is attacked by Cosmo, by his armies, and by wicked men - and the guilt of the whole world is heaped upon him - and he dies in agony in your place - - then you will understand more about the blend of justice and mercy. You will then see the terrible justice that the people of earth deserve - falling upon our kind and tender Prince. And you'll see the mercy that he deserves, coming to all who receive him as their Saviour.

When you see him take the death that was yours, and giving you the life that was his - - you will better understand that love is made of both justice and mercy.

Harry: Do all the people on the trillions of other planets understand this blend of justice and mercy now, or will they also have to wait until they see what we see?

Camero: The people on the other planets are learning with you Harry. They have never seen rebellion until you saw it. They have never seen death until you saw Cain kill his brother. The workings of Cosmo on earth is new to them also, and they are learning just like you are. Planet earth is the "Theater of the Universe."

Like you, the inhabitants of other worlds are watching with the deepest interest the events that are taking place on the earth.

Henry: It makes me sad as we see that most of the people on earth are being fooled into following Cosmo. His power to trick people is very great. His deceptive power here on earth is kinda like it was in the Great City. I couldn't believe how many hundreds of millions of the messengers were fooled into following him in the rebellious path of death. So maybe I shouldn't be too surprised that most of the people on earth are also being tricked into following him in his mad rebellion against the Great King.

Camero: Cosmo has been telling everyone in the universe that no one can obey the law of the Great King. In view of the rebellion of most people in the world, it may appear that he is right - even though he's wrong.

Harry: Then how is the Great King going to prove to the universe that Cosmo is a liar, and that everyone can truly and joyfully obey his law - like everyone did before Cosmo rebelled?

Camero: When the Great Prince leaves the City, he will lay down all his mighty power, and on the earth he will have no more power than any other baby - than any other child - than any other teenager - than any other man. And in that weakened condition, by clinging to his Father in constant prayer and trust, he will have power to obey the great law of the universe - just like you can have that power by doing the same, and by trusting in the merits of the Great Prince. That power is given to you by him as a gift.

Henry: Wow! That's all I can say. It's so simple. When the gift is so generous, and the power to obey and live is so free and easy to get, why most people are rejecting it is a mystery that is beyond me!

Camero: Yes, Henry. It's the same mystery that first showed itself in the Great City. It's called the "Mystery of Iniquity." There is no reason for it. There never will be.

Harry: I'm just thankful that not everyone on the earth is tricked into choosing to follow this monster Cosmo. Before Henry and I left the earth of the 21st century, I was fooled by this mad fiend myself. I can see that now. I shudder to think that the power that I was learning to use in the school for wizards was from him!

Camero: Look now boys. Cosmo is about to have a great conference meeting with his rebel armies. Let's zoom in ethereally and see what they are up to.

Cosmo: Hey hey you happy mole heads. Listen now to your mighty leader. You were blaming me when we first left that miserable city, but ain't you havin' fun now?

Maccaroni: Yea Cosmo, but I can't forget that we're going to be burned up and turn to ashes. Ain't we gonna be havin' fun then! We can fool the people of the earth, but we all know that we're not going to fool the Great King. The death penalty is coming to us for leading the whole world into ruin, and there's nothing we can do about it!

Cosmo: I told you dunces not to think about such things! I don't want to hear anyone talking like that again! Don't even think about our future. I want you to just think about now. Now is the time we must do all the damage we can. And we're being successful beyond our wildest dreams! Listen now. I've got a plan that we're going to carry out. What we're going to do is to fool so many people on this earth into joining us in rebelling against the King and his Prince that he will lose his patience and just wipe the whole place out. Hey hey! And when he rises in his majesty and destroys the whole world in his justice, then we can trick the rest of the planets into siding with us against him! Then we will have a legal right to take possession of those planets and hold them as our headquarters and our rightful prize.

We can't take control of the other planets unless they choose our way of thinking against the Great King. But we're going to give them a little help to join in our way of thinking. Hey hey! So now I want you smiling bird heads to go out to the world and double your efforts to make them steal, lie, and cheat each other. Make them do to each other what Cain did to Abel. Make them forget that there is any Great King. Make them think that he doesn't even exist. Make them think that the world got here by chance. Tell them that billions of years ago there was a great explosion and that everything in the universe came from that!

Saliva: Wait a minute Cosmo. The people on earth might be stupid, but they're not stupid enough to believe that no one planned the universe, and that it all got here by accident from some explosion! What if they ask where the matter came from that exploded? What then? Are we to get the people to blindly believe our lies without asking any questions? The people on earth still have brains. They are still over twelve feet tall, and they're still living to be over eight hundreds years old. The great grandson of Adam is still alive. Not only that - the garden of Eden containing the tree of life and the forbidden tree where you fooled Eve is still visible. The shining messengers from the hated city are still guarding those gates - - and how do you think we're going to trick people into thinking that the Great King doesn't even exist when the garden is still there, and those mighty guards at the gates are still in sight?

Cosmo: Yes - I'm telling you that you've got to get them to believe our lies without asking any questions you weed head. I'm going to trust that you can pull it off. Put forth your greatest power to get control of their brains, because if you don't trick these stooges into rebellion with us against the Great King, or into believing that he doesn't exist, then you will have to suffer for all the evil that they did in their lives. But if we fool them into joining us against the Great King and his Prince, then they will have to suffer for their own rebellion.

Somehow you've got to hide the love of the Great King from them. Blind them any way you can so they can't see his love. Get them killing more animals and eating their dead carcases with the blood in it so their blood streams will become feverish, and their minds will become inflamed, and they will lose their tempers, and kill each other. Animal blood will also inflame their passions so that they will steal their neighbor's wives, and take as many women as they please. Then, they'll be breaking the law of the Great King, and be plunged into guilt, and we'll have control of them all. Hey hey!

The love shown to them by the King in sending the Great Prince down here to die in their place, to save them from our power is the great thing that we hate. If you can once get their brains into a total state of rebellion, then you have power over them, and can then drag them lower and lower until they will be happy to think that the King doesn't exist. Then they'll ignore all the evidence that he does.

Once you get total control of their minds, you can drag them down until their cases will become hopeless. Then, they'll give up, and they'll be our slaves until they're dead. Hey hey!

Not only that, when the Prince comes down here, I'm looking forward to doing battle with him myself!

Just think you fools - if I can overcome him when he is a child or a teenager, and trick him into breaking the law of his Father in just one point, we've got him in our power forever, and the world and the universe will be ours! Hey hey!

Time goes quickly as Henry and Harry watch the unfolding of events. With amazement, the cousins watch as nearly 1500 years go by, and they see the world getting more and more corrupt under the fiendish hand of the first great rebel.

Cosmo: Hey hey you fiends! Look at the fun we're having now! Almost everyone is under our control, and the beautiful world that the Great King made is soon going to be a heap of ruins and a pile of dead bodies.

Maccaroni: Yea Cosmo, we're making people almost as miserable as we are.

Cosmo: Be quiet you dunce. I don't want to hear any of you talking like that. Live it up! I want to hear you living it up, and exalting that we are about to hurt the Great King and his Prince by hurting the creatures and the people that he made. That is our reward.

Warpo: Yea you guys. Cosmo's right. Eat drink, and be merry - for tomorrow we die.

Cosmo: **What did you say?**

Warpo: Oh ah - just scratch it out.

Cosmo: If I hear anyone talking like that again, I'll send him into outer space. Just do all the damage you can so we can hurt our enemy the Great Prince as much as possible. We will either rule this world or ruin it. Rule or ruin - that's our motto. Do you hear that you eel heads?

Now listen. I think we're getting close to our objective. I think the people of this world have gotten so bad that I wouldn't be surprised if the Great King loses his patience soon, and rises up any day now and wipes the whole place out. That's just what we want. We want to try to wear out his patience. If we can accomplish that, then, I can tell all the other planets that they have a tyrant for a ruler. Then, the planets will come over to us, and we'll compete with the Great King for the rulership of the universe!

Hey hey! Happy day, all the planets will soon be gray. Now I want you eggheads to go out and take possession of these people to make them forget the Great King and think that he doesn't exist. Get them to go off to work like animals each morning and never give him a thought.

If some of them won't forget him, then trick them into thinking that he is like us. Make them think that he's just waiting to find some fault in them so that he can punish them. Then the suckers will turn to me, and we can get control over their brains.

Do your best to stop people from praying to the Great King. We don't want them to pray. I know how he loves to answer their prayers, but the people of earth must not know that. If you can stop them from praying to him, then their power will be gone, and they'll think that he is like me, and that I'm like him. Hey hey!

My plan is that they'll all be mine. People of planet earth will either serve me, or they'll get the fate that I deserve. But with the help of you stooges, I'm going to pull off the greatest hoax the universe has ever seen.

I think it won't be long now until the patience of the Great King will be worn out, and then phase two of our great plan to take over the other planets will go into effect.

Slimehead: We're with you Cosmo. You're our great leader! We trust you to lead us because you're our only hope of happiness before we die.

Cosmo: What did you say?

Slimehead: Aaaah - just forget it.

Cosmo: One more time, and whoever does it will be sent back into Tartarus for a year until he learns his lesson!

With tears, Henry and Harry watch as the armies of Cosmo fulfil his wishes and kill animals; bring storms, hurricanes, earthquakes, tornados, fires, sickness, and death. The boys see these invisible forces taking control of the minds of men, women, and little children - causing them to have his spirit of selfishness; to make them jealous of each other, hurt each other, steal from each other, and kill one another.

Harry: Henry, in view of all the heartache, suffering and death we've been seeing Cosmo bring, there's no telling what would have happened if he hadn't been kicked out of the peaceful City.

Camero: You boys have seen the working of the great rebel for 1500 years, and in the misery and wickedness that now exists, you see a glimpse of what it would have been like in the Great City had not Cosmo been cast out.

Henry: Oh yes! But what a shame the mad fiend has filled the earth with violence!

Camero: Unfortunately, Cosmo's going to trick the people of earth into blaming the Great King for all this suffering. But you and I know - and Cosmo knows, that he has caused every bit of it!

Harry: He's not going to get away with it is he?

Camero: Oh no! His reward is coming. He knows it. From hearing them talk, you can tell that his fellow messengers are worried about it. And they truly have something to be worried about! That's why Cosmo keeps telling them to be quiet about the subject of their future death. He's trying to forget it because it causes him to tremble. He can't stand the thought. Anyone who follows him will share his fate. That's why there is no peace to the wicked, boys. No peace. In following the Great King and his Prince there's peace and joy.

Henry: Boy am I glad that at least a few people on earth are following our great Leaders. I sure am happy I've learned all these things. Just think Harry, at first we were scared to death when we got shot out into space and back into time from that terrible time machine, but now, I'm glad things have happened the way they have. If they hadn't, we would've been slaves of Cosmo ourselves - and wouldn't even know it!

Harry: You can say that again! The world is less than 1800 years old, and already it seems that the thoughts of men's hearts are only evil continually.

Camero: That's right Harry. Every emotion and imagination of nearly all of these poor people are at war with the divine principles of purity and peace and love. It is an example of what happens when Cosmo tricks people into rebelling against the holy law of the Great King.

Harry: Will Cosmo always be able to fool everyone into joining his rebellion?

Camero: No Harry. The Great King carries with him the sympathies and approval of the whole universe as step by step His great plan advances to its complete fulfillment. He will carry it with Him in the final eradication of rebellion. It will be seen that all who have forsaken the great law of the universe have placed themselves on the side of the great rebel. I will tell you that when this monster and his followers are judged, the whole universe will declare the Great King to be just and true.

For many years there were two separate classes of people in the world, and they stayed away from each other. But finally, the race of Cain, {controlled by Cosmo}, spreading from the place of their first settlement, scattered over the plains and valleys where the children of Seth were living. The descendants of Seth, in order to escape from the rebellious influence of the children of Cain, went up into the mountains, and made their homes there. As long as this separation continued, they maintained the worship of the Great King in its purity.

But as time passed, they began to mingle, little by little, with the inhabitants of the valleys. The descendants of Seth were attracted to the beautiful women of the descendants of Cain. They dated them, and finally started marrying them. And the women descendants of Seth were attracted to the handsome muscle men among the descendants of Cain. But they had no clue that these associations would lead to horrible and deadly results.

The cousins are in agony as they watch this, but there's nothing they can do about it.

Camero: Look boys, now the children of Seth are losing their peace of mind and the sweet spirit of obedience to the Great King. They're taking on the cold, selfish character of Cain and of Cosmo. Humans will learn the hard way that they will become like whoever they mingle with. Boys, I want to tell you that it is dangerous - very dangerous - for a follower of the Great King to hang around with followers of Cosmo just to have a good time. Yes, there are times when they must be with them - to tell the slaves of Cosmo of the beauty of their King, and the joy that comes from following him. They must help Cosmo's slaves learn of the freedom that the Great Prince offers them from Cosmo's awful rule. But the followers of Seth are not mingling with the followers of Cain for those reasons. They're hanging around them to have a good time, and to marry their beautiful women, and their handsome muscle men. We see that they are headed for disaster as Cosmo is taking control of their minds. The fiend is making them his slaves.

Cosmo: Hey hey you peanut heads! Watch the brains of the followers of the Great King get warped! I'm taking control of the suckers and they don't even know it! Come you pin heads, see some more of my gorgeous women and muscle men!

The cousins are weeping as they watch the children of Seth mingle for so long with the children of Cain that they become like them. Now, instead of trying to lead the slaves of Cosmo to the joy of following the Great King, the people - all mingled together in the first great ecumenical movement, fix their minds upon worldly pleasure and enjoyment. They forgot all about the great law of the universe by which they are being tested to see if they will be worthy to sit on gorgeous,

glittering thrones with the Great King to joyfully co-rule the universe - and never die. This makes Cosmo laugh with glee.

Cosmo: Now's our chance you frog heads. Now

that I've made these poor earthlings forget that they're being tested by the law of the universe, you can now start to fool and trick them into believing that the Great King doesn't exist! Hey hey! Some of you asked me how you were going to do it. Our time has come! Now we can pull it off! Go to work you beanheads, and don't come back till the whole world thinks that there is no Great King, and that everything got here by a mindless big bang explosion - and then I'll rule their mindless minds without limit. Hey hey!

Wormwood: Alright Cosmo. We'll do it.

Let's go boys. There are hundreds of millions of us. We'll range around the earth, and we'll give the people the pleasures they love. We'll keep them partying and lying, and cheating, and stealing, and killing, and we'll give them gold and silver, and money, and women, and wine, and song, and they'll eat the carcases of dead animals with the red, juicy blood in it. We'll make them blood-thirsty, and they'll forget the Great King, and believe that He doesn't exist, and they'll never know that they're all headed for the pit. Ready or not - - here we come!

Evil now spreads around the world like a deadly leprosy. For nearly a thousand years Adam lives among men, a witness to the results of disobeying the great law of the universe. Faithfully he tries to stem the tide of evil. Faithfully he tries to teach his descendants the way of righteousness and purity. The giant and lordly Adam carefully treasures what the Great Prince has revealed to him, and he repeats it to succeeding generations.

Cosmo: Listen you egg heads, this Adam is keeping us from our plan. He keeps telling people about the Great King and how he is going to send his Son to come to earth to die in their places so that they can live and not die. And he keeps telling them how the Great Prince will come here and give them power to obey the law of the Great King and be free from our power! Horrors! As long as this goes on, our plans cannot succeed! You've got to kill Adam you fiends. Go and do it at once!

Chiahee: How?

Cosmo: I don't care. Do it any way you please.

Hagwart: We've tried Cosmo. We've tried! But the Great Prince has put a wall of his messengers all around him. We can't get close to him. Not only that, there are other trouble-makers that we can't get to either. We control nearly everyone in the world, but there are some like Adam who have this wall of messengers from the celestial city all around them, and they keep driving us back.

Cosmo: What methods have you tried you dunces?

Hagwart: We've tried going up to these people directly to do away with them, but we couldn't get close. Then, we tried to inspire the followers of Cain to do away with them, but the shining messengers always do something to stop our slaves from hurting them.

Cosmo: Well, keep trying, you bean heads. The day Adam is dead is the day that our plans can start to be perfected.

Cosmo and his mob couldn't kill Adam. He lived to be 930 years old. He saw his grandchildren to the ninth generation. To them, he described man's holy and happy state in Paradise. He repeated to them the history of his fall, telling them of the sufferings by which the Great King had taught him the necessity of strict obedience to His law of love, and explaining to them the merciful provisions for their salvation from eternal death. Unfortunately, not many would listen to his words. Often he was met with bitter reproaches for the sin that had brought such woe upon the world.

Adam's life was one of humility and sorrow for what he had done. When he left Eden, the thought that he must die thrilled him with horror. Filled with the keenest remorse for his own sin, and doubly bereaved in the death of Abel and the rejection of Cain, Adam was bowed down with anguish.

Though the sentence of death pronounced upon Adam had at first appeared terrible, yet after seeing for nearly a thousand years the results of rebellion and suffering caused by Cosmo, he felt that it was merciful of the Great King to bring to an end a life of sorrow and pain.

Time moves on - with the world getting worse and worse as Cosmo tries his best to get wicked men by the millions to wear out the patience of the Great King - and abandon planet earth to the rebel army.

Camero: Boys, Adam is nearly a thousand years old now, and Cosmo knows that he is going to die soon. This makes him happy, since messengers of light have been protecting him. The great rebel has been hoping to trick the world into believing that the Great King doesn't exist. He thinks that after Adam is gone, he can do it more easily. He knows that if he can do it, he will have total, complete control over the entire world, and the Great King will have to leave the planet to his cruel and insane rule. But what Cosmo doesn't know is that if that ever happened, it would mean death to the world. The rule of Cosmo ends in death because he has death in him. If Cosmo ruled everyone, he himself would eventually kill off the very people over whom he ruled. Either that, or their lives would became so unbearable under Cosmo's cruelty, that they would kill themselves.

Henry: I can see that! But it looks like more and more people on earth are being fooled into following Cosmo, and it looks like soon, his insane plans might succeed - especially after Adam dies. How will the Great King stop it?

Camero: Our King has other faithful people besides Adam. Seven generations have been born now since the world was made, and the seventh descendant from Adam is named Enoch. Have you noticed him boys? He is just as strong to defend the law of the Great King as Adam is.

Adam now dies, and is buried by his family and friends. They mourn. There has never been a man like this - who had no mother, but was formed from the dust of the earth by the hands of the Great Creator himself. This kind and gentle giant of a man will be missed. With Adam gone, Cosmo's forces redouble their efforts to corrupt the world and get total control of it.

Cosmo: Hey hey you mosquito heads. Now that Adam is out of the way, redouble your efforts to trick people into believing that the Great King doesn't exist. Not only that, I want you to fool people into thinking that I don't exist either.

Slimehead: What good will it do Cosmo for people to think that you don't exist? I thought you wanted everyone in the world to worship you. How are they going to worship you if they think you don't exist?

Cosmo: Of course I wouldn't expect you ant heads to understand that. It would take a brain like mine to understand such an ingenious plan. Listen now - and I'll tell you the beauty of this plan. Here it is. If the people of earth don't believe that I exist, it will help them to believe that the Great King doesn't exist either. Hey hey! And that's what we want! You can't have one without the other. Adam has been telling people that there are two great forces - good and evil. He's been telling them that the Great King and his Prince are the force of good, and that I am the great force of evil. Well, if a person believes that there is no great force of evil, then he doesn't need to believe that there is a great force of good. Is that clear to your tiny brains?

Not only that - if people don't believe that I exist, it will actually help me take control of them easier, and worship me without even knowing it. Hey hey!

Smorman: How - great one?

Cosmo: How? Whoever obeys me worships me. Whoever obeys the Great King worships him. Obedience is the highest form of worship. Do you frog heads comprehend that?

Smorman: I see it now! Cosmo, you're a genius.

Cosmo: Of course!

Enoch lived sixty-five years, and had a son. After that, he walked and talked with the Great Prince for three hundred years. During these earlier years Enoch had loved and feared the Great King and had kept His commandments. From the lips of Adam he had learned the dark story of the Fall, and the cheering one of the love given to the people of planet earth, as seen in the promise that the Great Prince would come to earth one day to die in man's place, and save him from Cosmo's power, and from eternal death. Enoch joyfully believed the wonderful news, and relied upon the Redeemer to come. But after the birth of his first son, Enoch reached a higher experience. He was drawn into a closer relationship with his great Leader - who at times, appeared to him and talked with him.

As Enoch saw his child's love for its father, its simple trust in his protection; as he felt the deep, yearning tenderness of his own heart for that first-born son, he learned a precious lesson of the wonderful love of the Great King to men in the gift of His Son, and the confidence which the people of earth may have in their great Father who lives in the center of the universe. The unfathomable love of the King through his Prince became the subject of Enoch's meditations day and night; and with all the fervor of his soul he sought to reveal that love to the people among whom he lived.

Camero: Boys, I want you to notice that Enoch hasn't become a hermit, shutting himself away from the world; for he has a work to do for the people. You see that he is a kind and loving husband and father, a friend, and citizen.

Harry: What a relief to watch people like Enoch

after seeing so many who are so cold and hard, and cruel. It appears that most people are unfitting their own selves to sit on thrones with the Great King - and if they were taken to the gorgeous, celestial city, they'd want to get out of there and go wherever Cosmo was so they could practice their corruptions and lusts.

Camero: That's right Harry. They are on probation, and they don't know it. Each person is going to get the reward that he wants most. If he really longs to be in an atmosphere of love, obedience, and kindness - as it is in the Great City, he will be there. How? - through the future death of the Great Prince in his place. But if he wants to live a life of corruption and make his own self the center of everything - caring nothing for others or for the great law of love, then he would choose the kingdom of Cosmo. And he would actually choose the same reward that Cosmo is going to have - death.

Harry: You mean they would choose death rather to live where the Great King and Prince are?

Camero: The Great Prince said, "All they that hate me love death." That's a very true statement.

Now I want you boys to remember two things.

1) "The wages of sin is death." Death is what Cosmo and all who choose to follow his way of rebellion

will earn as their rightful pay. Death is what they have worked for. They have earned it as the wages of their work.

2) The gift of the Great King is eternal life through his anointed son. Those who choose him and the way of his law, will not receive the death which they have earned. They will receive the eternal life that the Great Prince has earned.

Harry: Wow! What a deal! Knowing this, who on earth would ever choose the disobedient and deadly path of Cosmo?

Camero: Almost everyone!

Henry: Gasp!

Camero: Nearly the whole world will choose death Harry. You can look around the world which you've been watching for over 1500 years, and you can see it.

Henry: What a mystery!

Camero: It lies in the heart of man. When king Adam chose to fail the one tiny test that he was given, he actually turned the kingship of the world over to Cosmo. From that moment, Cosmo took control of the nature of man, and gave him his own selfish, proud, disobedient nature. So man now needs a power outside of himself to resist the power of Cosmo - because man has the same nature inside of him that Cosmo does. That's why the offer of the Great Prince to die in man's place, and to give people of earth his own divine nature of love and unselfishness as a free gift, is so important. It means life or death whether or not people take that wonderful free offer.

Henry: Yea. I can see why Cosmo is so desperate to keep people from even finding out what you just said, and from understanding it. No wonder he's been getting people to drink alcohol, and to use drug weeds that cause their brains to get foggy.

Camero: Cosmo is insane himself, and he's desperate to kill as many people as he can, and take them into death with him. And he's been having pretty good success. But if people reject the kind offer of the Great Prince, and end up in death with Cosmo, it's their own choice boys. It's their own fault. Most people do not want a new heart of unselfishness and love. Most people want to live for pleasure and fun, and to do as they please - without the restraint of the law of the universe upon them. That is some of the secret of Cosmo's power over them boys. Do you understand that? People could have the power of the Great King to break away from Cosmo's deadly force if they really wanted it. Most people don't want it. Cosmo has fooled and tricked them into not wanting deliverance from him, and from the pleasures and corruptions which they love. That's why more people don't take the help that the Great King and Prince are so generously holding out to them. That's why you see the world getting so corrupt. If the people would only ask the Great King for help, he will gladly give it to them! Oh how gladly he would hear their prayers - and forgive them, and give them peace of mind, and joy, and power to obey, and freedom from Cosmo's power to torment their minds. Then how happy they'd be! They'd be like Enoch.

Harry: Will the Great King keep holding out his mercy to them forever?

Camero: Cosmo knows that the answer to that is "no," and he's trying to hold his control over the people until they pass over the line of probation, and the mercy of the Great King is exhausted - like it was for him in the Great City. Then, Cosmo hopes to control the minds of the poor people until they're dead.

Henry: Oh no! What will be the end of all this horrible, invisible battle for the minds of planet earth?

Chapter Thirteen

"The Surprise"

Camero: Boys, the wickedness of the people on earth has reached such a height that they are in danger of crossing over the line I told you about, and causing destruction to finally be pronounced against them.

Harry: But isn't that what Cosmo wants? Won't that go right along with his plot to win the sympathies of the other planets against the Great King?

Camero: It seems that Cosmo has the Great King in a trap. It seems that he will win - whatever the Great King does. If he destroys all the wicked people on the earth, Cosmo will complain to the other planets that the King is a cruel tyrant who kills people. That way he hopes to win their sympathies. Then he hopes to take control of them and use their planets as his headquarters in this great battle.

On the other hand, if the Great King does nothing and allows things to take their natural course - with Cosmo forcing his insane control over everything and nearly everybody on earth, he will eventually get his cruel and bloodthirsty people to murder all the kind and good people - - and Cosmo will have a total victory that way.

Harry: So what will the Great King do?

Camero: Watch just a little longer Harry. You're going to see for yourself.

Deeper and deeper grows the tide of human guilt. Darker and darker gather the clouds of divine judgment. Yet Enoch, the witness of faith, is holding on his way, warning, pleading, entreating, striving to turn back the tide of guilt and to stay the bolts of vengeance. Though his warnings are disregarded by a pleasure-loving, sinful, people, he has the testimony which the Great King approves, and he continues to battle faithfully against the prevailing wickedness.

Harry: Will Cosmo succeed in killing Enoch like he has killed so many others?

Camero: No. I've been informed that something special is about to happen. Cosmo has tried to make people believe that there is no good reward for the righteous, and no eternal death for the wicked. He has told his evil messengers to go out and make some people believe that everyone will die and that will be the end of them. Others, he has made to believe that everyone will go and live in the Great City - both good and evil. He has gotten nearly everyone to believe one of these two lies. But the Great King is going to do something that will open the eyes of the people and give hope to those who are trying to obey his law of love.

Harry: What will happen?

Camero: It's time now. Follow me. We're going to go with Enoch to a place where he is speaking to the people. He is still pleading with them to follow the law of the Great King instead of the selfish ways of Cosmo. Listen now to his words.

The boys and Camero listen and watch as Enoch pleads with the great crowd of people who have gathered around him. Some are mocking. Some are laughing. Some of crying. Some are glad that they are hearing what they know to be the truth.

Most of the people mock the folly of him who doesn't seek gold or silver. Enoch's heart is on eternal treasures. In his heart, he has looked by faith upon the great, celestial city. By faith, he has seen the King in His glory. His mind, his heart, his conversation, are there. The greater the existing corruption, the more earnest is his longing for the home of the Great King.

For three centuries Enoch has walked and talked with the Great Prince and his messengers. Day by day he has longed for a closer union; nearer and nearer has grown the communion, until -

Henry: Look! Look at Enoch! He going up!

Enoch has stood at the threshold of the eternal world, only a step between himself and the land of paradise.

Now Enoch's walk with the Great Prince, so long pursued on earth, continues - - and all of a sudden - surrounded by invisible, shining messengers - Enoch rises up into the sky as the dumbfounded crowd of people look at him, and in a twinkle - he's gone.

At warp speed, flashing billions of light years - past galaxies, flaming constellations, shining nebulas - Enoch finally goes in through the gates of the Great City – the first from among men to enter there - having never died.

Henry: Wow! I don't believe it! This is wonderful! I know this took Cosmo, and the poeple, and everyone by surprise! No one expected the Great King to do this! Enoch never died! He's the first person who never died!

Harry: This sure sheds light on the characters of both the Great King and Cosmo. They're both on trial before the whole universe, and I know who's going to win!

Enoch's loss was felt on earth. The voice that had been heard day after day in warning and instruction was missed. Some from among both the righteous and the wicked went looking for him. Thinking that he might have been taken to one of his secret places, those who loved him looked very carefully, but couldn't find him. They reported that he didn't exist - for the Great King had taken him away!

Camero: Boys, by the translation of Enoch to the Great City, the Great King plans to teach an important lesson. There's danger that people will get discouraged because of the fearful results of Adam's sin. Many are ready to say, "What good is it that we've obeyed the law of the Great King since a heavy curse is resting upon the earth, and death is coming to everyone?"

But by taking Enoch to the Great City without ever dying, the Great King has swept away the gloom, and has given hope to people of earth. He wants to show even those who don't love him that as through Adam came death, so through the promised Deliverer - whom Enoch trusted in - comes life with no end.

Harry: Great! Just imagine how Enoch feels now! He's in the Great City - knowing that he's there safe, and he's there forever. Man! He must be as happy as a lark!

Camero: Yes, he is very happy, and he's hoping that many others will be able to join him there so that the millions of gigantic mansions will be filled up.

Henry: What gigantic mansions?

Camero: The Great King is making them just for the people of earth to live in when they get there. Have you forgotten that he plans that all of you should take the places of the millions of messengers who fell with Cosmo?

Harry: Oh that's right! If we keep that thought in mind, it'll help us understand why the Great King and Prince do a lot of things in dealing with people.

Camero: Cosmo has been urging upon people the belief that there is no reward for the righteous or punishment for the wicked, and that it is impossible for people to obey the divine law. But in the case of Enoch, the Great King shows that He rewards those who diligently seek Him.

In taking Enoch to the City of paradise without ever dying, the Great King shows what He will do for anyone and everyone who trust in him and keep His commandments. Isn't that good news?

Henry: You can say that again!

Harry: Cool!

Camero: Not only that, through this gift to Enoch, people are taught that it is truly possible to obey the law of the universe even while living in the midst of corruption. Cosmo has been yelling that it's impossible. Enoch has proven him a liar.

Henry: Woopeee!

Harry: Henry, this act of taking Enoch out of this world before he died also answers another question which we asked Camero while we were in the City. We asked him what we had to do to live there. Remember?

Henry: Oh yea. I remember that. Time goes so fast! It seems like a thousand years since we've been in the city.

Harry: It has been over a thousand years! Now we know that all we have to do to live in the Great City one day is to live like Enoch lived. All we have to do Henry is to live in a close relationship with the Great King and our Prince, receiving his power as a gift to joyfully obey his law of love. It's that simple!

Henry: Man! I feel like shouting for joy!

Meanwhile, Cosmo and his mob of murderers have regrouped - out of sight - to see what they can do about the "disappearance" of Enoch.

Muldoon: Alright Cosmo! Now what're we gonna do? Here goes Enoch up into the city that we can't even get into. He's taken our place! I overheard one of the messengers from there tell a friend of his that the

Great King is intending to fill our places in the City with people from the earth. I don't like that! What are we going to do about this Cosmo?

Cosmo: We're going to stop it if I have anything to do with it. When I get through with this planet, I'll be king of it forever, and none of my earth slaves will even want to go there. Why - - with no bloody carcases to eat, no alcohol, no fighting, fussing, drugs, or wild orgies, their brains will be in withdrawal - - jumping, jerking, jiving, and the Great City would be too dull for them. I'll push their brains "out of control" and make them so selfish that if they don't get their own way, they'll get angry. I'll cause them to have fights, wars, terror, murders, chaos, and then blame the Great King for it all! Hey hey! I'll turn their brains into a pin-ball machine. I'll give them so much pleasure that these goons would be miserable in the city with none of their exciting thrills.

Don't worry you eggheads, they'll never see the place! The world has chosen me as their master - the Great Cosmo! Enoch slipped through the cracks, but you slackers must redouble your efforts to see that the brains of these crawdads are in such a condition that they would never want to get near the City of the Great King! Hey hey!

Molehead: But the news about Enoch is spreading around the world like wildfire Cosmo! How are we gonna erase this thing out of the minds of the people. What'll we do!

Cosmo: Be quiet you mole head. You're talking like we have a problem. The great Cosmo has no problems that he can't handle. What we're going to do is to ignore it. Do all you can to minimize it. Get people to forget it. Tell 'em it was nothing. We control their brains anyway. I don't want this to lead to any of our people turning to the Great King. We must not let that happen! Put your noose more tightly around their necks. Make men mad and thirsty for more and more blood. Make them so they don't even want to go where Enoch went. Then we'll control them more than before.

Now get going! I don't want to hear any of you telling me about more earthlings who got away. By the time the Great Prince comes here in human form to try to save them from my power, I'll have them in such a state that they'll tell him to go back where he came from. Hey hey!

About this time a baby is born. His name is Noah. In the days of Noah a double curse is resting upon the earth in consequence of Adam's sin, and of the murder committed by Cain. Yet this has not greatly changed the face of nature. There are signs of decay, but the earth is still rich and beautiful in the gifts of the Great King. The hills are still crowned with majestic trees supporting the fruit-laden branches of the vine. Vast, gardenlike plains are clothed with blankets of green, and sweet with the fragrance of a million flowers. The fruits of the earth are in great variety, and almost without limit. The trees far surpass in size, beauty, and perfect proportion any to be found in the twenty first century from which the boys came. Their wood is of fine grain and hard substance, closely resembling stone, and hardly less enduring. Gold, silver, and precious stones are found in abundance - lying all over the ground.

The human race yet retains much of its early vigor. Only a few generations have passed since Adam had access to the tree which was to prolong life forever; and man's existence is still measured by centuries. There are many giants – men of great height and strength, famous for wisdom, skillful in devising the most cunning and wonderful works; but their guilt in giving loose rein in rebellion to the law of the universe is in proportion to their skill and mental ability.

As the boys look around the earth, they see that the people are using the gold, silver, precious stones and choice wood in the construction of gorgeous mansions for themselves, and are trying to outdo each other in beautifying their homes with the most skillful workmanship. But they seek only to gratify the desires of their own proud hearts, and revel in scenes of pleasure, lust, and wickedness. Not desiring to keep the Great King in their minds, many of them have finally come to deny His existence – just what Cosmo has been working and hoping for.

Cosmo: Congratulations you happy pinheads! You finally pulled it off. Now with Adam and Enoch gone, you've been able to get the masses to think that the Great King doesn't exist. Hey hey!

Camero: Look boys. People are adoring nature in place of the One who made it. They are glorifying human genius, worshiping the works of their own hands, and are teaching their children to bow down to carved images.

Henry: For years we've sensed that something awful is coming because of the horrific corruption. We've almost felt like holding our breaths to see what will come. What will happen now?

Camero: I've just received a communication from the City. I've been told that the Great King wants to tell us all something important. I'm going to leave you for a short time. I'll be back soon. I get a sense that whatever is going to happen is going to happen fast. Don't worry about Cosmo. He can't hurt you or get to you. Keep your eyes on the situation. I'll see you shortly.

Camero now joins the vast armies of his fellow messengers as they gather for a great meeting in front of the throne of the Great King and Prince.

They are greeted by their King, and encouraged to continue their good work for the poor people of earth who are being murdered and ruined by Cosmo's insane power.

Then, the Great Prince stands before them and speaks. His face beams with love and compassion. He starts out in a slow, kindly voice which is distinctly heard by the hundreds of millions standing before him in the outer court of the massive and gorgeous temple. Every ear is bent to catch his every word.

Great Prince: The Great King has seen for quite some time now that the wickedness of man is great in the earth, and that every imagination of the thoughts of his heart is only evil continually. The earth is also corrupt before him, and filled with violence. Cosmo has mutated both plants and animals, and has caused briars, thorns, and strange, large, powerful, and dangerous animals to be mutated into existence which the Great King did not make in the beginning. Cosmo has gone all out to drag people down to the dust, and has even dared to fill them with such lust as to mate with animals - resulting in degraded and strange beings who are living in caves. In doing this, men have crossed over the line. If something is not done, the human race will eventually become part human and part animal, and every trace of the divine nature will be blotted out of humanity. Then their cases will become hopeless.

Your King has given men His commandments as a rule of life, but his law is being willfully and constantly broken, and every conceivable sin and suffering is the result. The wickedness of men is open and daring. Justice is trampled in the streets, and the cries of the oppressed are reaching unto the City itself.

Cosmo has introduced polygamy, contrary to the divine arrangement, and this also is causing much misery, jealousy, murder, strife, and corruption. Neither the marriage relation nor the rights of property are respected. Whoever wants the wives or possessions of his neighbor, takes them by force, and men exult in their deeds of violence. They delight in destroying the life of animals; and the use of their cooked, bloody, dead carcases for food renders them still more cruel and bloodthirsty, until they have come to regard human life with astonishing indifference.

The messengers stand breathless as they listen. They know that something awesome is about to happen.

Great Prince: The world is in its infancy; yet iniquity has become so deep and widespread that the Great King can no longer bear with it. He has said to me - "I will destroy man whom I have created from the face of the earth." He has declared that His Spirit will not always strive with the guilty race. If they will not cease to pollute with their sins the world and its rich treasures, He will blot them from His creation, and will destroy the things with which He has delighted to bless them. He will sweep away the strange mutations of half man and half animal. He will sweep away the giant, murderous mutated animals, and Cosmo will not be permitted to totally corrupt and destroy the good of the earth. The Great King will step in and do something to put a halt to Cosmo's insane work of depravity. He will save what is good in man and animals from total annihilation.

Millions of messengers are weeping. This gathering reminds them of another meeting -

when such a pronouncement was made against rebellious Cosmo - while he stood in the vast crowd surrounding the royal throne in the Great City nearly two thousand years earlier.

The messengers are told the particulars of how this judgment will be carried out. They are informed that there is a man who is faithful to the law of the Great King like Enoch was, and that through him, the royal plan to save the world from total destruction from the power of Cosmo will be carried out. His name is Noah.

Camero now flies quickly back to join the boys as they watch the developments on earth in the great battle over planet earth.

Camero: Boys, now I know what is going on, and what is going to happen. Are you ready?

Henry: We can hardly wait. I can sense that whatever it is will be awesome.

Camero informs the boys concerning all that he has learned in the presence of the Great King and Prince.

They are told that a messenger from the

courts of light has been commissioned to fly quickly to Noah - {the tenth descendant from Adam} - to tell him what to do in the great plan to preserve what good is left in the world, and to deliver all obedient people from being murdered by men transformed to demons.

It's revealed to the boys that the messenger has directed Noah to build a gigantic ship on dry ground - called an "ark."

Harry: Wow!

While building the ark, Noah is to tell everyone who will listen that the Great King will bring a massive flood of water upon the earth to destroy all who are not inside. But since everyone is invited to come inside, only those who refuse to believe the message, or who don't value their lives, will die.

Henry: What if everyone believes the message and wants to go inside the ark? How will the ark hold all those millions of people?

Camero: I was informed that if everyone will

believe the message and turn from their rebellion against the Great King and his law, that he will tell Noah to announce that because everyone are turning away from their rebellion, the flood will be called off and will not come.

Boys, this is a test for the world. Those who get into the ark show that they are putting their trust in the Great King to save them from death. They're also showing that they will obey Him. On the other hand, those who refuse to enter the ark, show that they have no faith in the Great King to save them from rebellion and death. They show that they are the ones who are willfully disobedient, and who would still be disobedient if they were permitted to live. By this simple test, the Great King will separate the wicked from the good people who - after the flood will populate the earth.

Both the strange and dangerous human and animal mutations will be swept away, and will not corrupt the earth as Cosmo has been planning that they will. He will be disappointed.

Harry: I don't feel sorry for Cosmo and his wicked plans - one bit.

Henry: Me neither! The only way the Great King and Prince can win in this universal battle is for Cosmo and his rebels to be totally disappointed forever. The sooner, the better.

Camero: As I speak, Noah is receiving the exact dimensions of the ark and explicit directions in regard to its construction in every particular. Human wisdom could not have devised a structure of so great strength and durability. The Great King himself is the designer, and Noah the master builder.

Harry: Wow!

Henry: What I see is that this thing is going to be a tremendous solution to the many horrible plots of Cosmo. His plan to totally corrupt and kill every good person and wipe them from the face of the earth is going to be stopped. Is that right?

Camero: That's right.

Harry: Camero, will you please explain a little about the ark to us? What will it be like?

Camero: It will be constructed like the hull of a great ship that it might float - even with the immense waves crashing against it. Water will cover the entire world! It will take a colossal ship to withstand the mighty storm that will come – so great a storm that it will be like nothing the world has ever seen. But in some respects the ark will resemble a house. It will be three stories high, with only one door. That will be in the side. The light will be admitted at the top, and the different apartments will be so arranged that all will receive light. The material to be used in the construction of the ark will be the cypress, or gopher wood, which will be untouched by decay for hundreds of years. The building of this immense structure will be a slow process. And because of the great size of the trees and the extremely hard nature of the wood, much more labor will be required to prepare timber than it would be in the twenty-first century A.D. even with the greater strength of the twelve to fifteen foot men who live now. All that men can do will be done to make the work perfect, yet the ark cannot of itself withstand the fearsome storm which is coming. The Great King alone can preserve His servants upon the wild and raging waters.

The boys intently watch as Noah invests all that he owns in building the ark. As he begins to construct this immense ship on dry ground, great crowds come from every direction to see the strange sight, and to hear the earnest, fervent words of the peculiar preacher. Every blow struck upon the ark is a witness to the people.

Many at first appear to receive the warning; yet they don't turn to the Great King with true sorrow for their sins. They are not willing to put them away - and during the time that goes by before the coming of the great flood, their faith is tested, and they fail to endure the trial. Overcome by the prevailing unbelief, they finally join their former friends in rejecting the solemn message.

Some are deeply convicted, and would have heeded the words of warning; but there are so many to jest and ridicule, that they partake of the same spirit, resist the invitations of mercy, and are soon among the boldest and most defiant scoffers -- for none are so reckless and go to such lengths in evil as do those who have once had light, but have resisted the convictions of their conscience.

Camero: Boys, not everyone in this generation worship idols. Many claim to be worshipers of the Great King. They claim that their idols made of carved wood or stone are just to remind people of the Great King, and that through them, the people will get a clearer conception of him.

But we see that this class are leading out in rejecting the preaching of Noah. As they try to represent the Great King by their senseless carvings, their minds are blinded to His majesty and power. This thing of having images in churches will also be copied by a large class of worshipers who will live down in the twenty-first century where you came from.

As rebellion against the great law of the universe has become widespread, the people's evil ways appear less and less sinful to themselves, and many of their religious leaders have finally declared that the divine law is no longer in force. That is just what Cosmo has been inspiring them to teach. His rebel armies have finally been able to trick most of the people into believing that it is against the character of the Great King to punish rebellion. Because of this false idea, they say that it is therefore impossible for a great flood to come to destroy the wicked.

Henry: What a lie! Cosmo is behind it all. But his poor deceived slaves seem no more able to see through his tricks than the millions of messengers in the Great City whom he fooled into following him in the first place.

Harry: I'm glad to know that anyone who is honest won't be fooled by this insane fiend. Isn't that right Camero?

Camero: That's exactly right. The Great King protects anyone who really wants it, from Cosmo's torturous power - no matter how weak they are.

As the ark takes shape, the strange phenomenon grabs the attention of the entire world. But because of their leaders, the masses have turned against the justice and laws of the Great King, and Noah is regarded as a wild fanatic.

Henry: Listen to them mocking! Noah must have a lot of patience to not get upset with all these people as they're yelling, laughing, and interrupting him so rudely while he's trying to speak.

Harry: I admire him for it. Anyone who is in tune with the kind spirit of the Great King would be able to see what a kind man Noah is. Any honest people will be able to see that he's just trying to help save the people from coming death.

Henry: But where can you find an honest man! From the way people are treating him, it seems as though they don't see anything. It seems like their brains have been so debauched by Cosmo that they don't care whether they die or not!

Out of sight, many divisions of a massive

army assemble in the blackness - just above the earth's atmosphere.

COSMO: Hey hey you doomed dunces! I've got your brains, and Noah can't get them back!

GO ahead my faithful slaves - - tighten the noose around the necks of these stooges. But mark my words - don't let me hear of any of them getting into that ark – ya hear me!

Carbuncle: Yes great master! We'll not let them go until their dead bodies litter the ground.

Camero: Boys, I want to tell you something important. When Cosmo tempted Eve to disobey the Great King, he said to her, "You will not surely die." That was the first great lie. And he's telling it again to everyone, and giving it as a reason for people not to get into the ark. The fiend has tricked the great and wise men of the world so much with this lie that they are yelling it at Noah while he's speaking. Listen -

Pastor Rolin Rock. Listen to me everyone! The threatenings of the Great King are for the purpose of intimidating you and will never happen. You need not be alarmed. The Great King loves the world too much to do it. Such an event as the destruction of the world by the one who made it, and the punishment of the beings He has created, will never happen! Be at peace. You have nothing to fear! Noah is a wild fanatic!

A thunderous roar goes up from the crowd.

The world makes merry at the folly of the "deluded old man." Instead of humbling their hearts with gratitude that a way of escape from death is being offered them, the masses continue their wickedness the same as though the warning had never been given.

But Noah stands like a rock amid the tempest. Surrounded by popular contempt and ridicule, he distinguishes himself by his unwavering faithfulness.

A power attends his words, for it is the voice of the Great King to man through His servant.

Harry: Camero, how is Noah able to take all

this mocking and still be sweet and kind to these people?

Camero: Daily connection with the Great King through prayer has made him strong in the strength of infinite power.

Cosmo: Hey hey you happy goons. Keep blasting these twiddleheads with your power until their brains are like jelly. But make them so angry at Noah that they'll kill him and he'll never get into the ark himself!

The boys watch the progress of the battle for the minds of the people, as for one hundred and twenty years the solemn voice of Noah falls on the ears of that generation in regard to events, which, so far as human wisdom can judge, are impossible.

Cosmo is successful in getting the people to reason that for centuries the laws of nature have been fixed. The recurring seasons have come in their order. Rain has never fallen. The earth has been watered by a gentle mist, and still has nearly the same gorgeous beauty it had when Adam lived. The rivers have never passed their boundaries, but have carried their waters safely to the sea. Fixed decrees have kept the waters from overflowing their banks.

But the masses - blinded by the reasoning of their leaders, {which they have gotten from Cosmo}, don't recognize the hand of Him who has given the waters their boundaries.

Camero: Boys, we see that as time has been passing with no apparent change in nature, men whose hearts have at times trembled with fear, are beginning to be re-assured. You hear their religious leaders telling them to relax - - to go back to their work and forget about a flood which they say will "never come." We see them continuing to go to their wild parties and gluttonous feasts. They're eating, drinking, and making plans for the future - not knowing that they will soon be dead. More - they are going to greater lengths in wickedness, and in defiant disregard of the requirements of the Great King than ever. Their words against Noah are getting more violent. They are clearly showing that they have no fear of one who is infinite in power.

Professor Mork: Listen to me everyone! If there was any truth in what Noah is saying, the men of science, the wise, the prudent, the great men, would understand the matter.

Probation for the world is about to close. Noah has faithfully followed the instructions he has received. The ark is finished in every particular, and is stored with food for many people and animals.

And now the King's faithful servant makes his last solemn appeal as he stands on the dirt-stained platform where he has stood for over a hundred years. With an agony of desire that words cannot express, he pleads with the people - whom he loves - to seek a refuge while it might be found.

At this, Henry can't take it any more. He raises his arms and screams out -

Henry: Get into the ark people! Please! Go into the ark!

Camero: They can't hear you Henry. If they won't hear Noah, they wouldn't hear you.

Again they reject Noah's words, and raise their voices in jest and scoffing.

Howy Biglor: You've been buildin' this ark and preachin' on doom for a long time now. When's our doom comin'? Today?

The crowd roars with laughter.

Suddenly a silence falls on the mocking mob. Animals of every description are seen coming from mountain and forest, and quietly making their way toward the ark. A noise as of a rushing wind was heard. Messengers, invisible to the people, are leading them to the ark. Most of the giant and dangerous land creatures which Cosmo has mutated from peaceful animals - and which will later be called "dinosaurs" - are left outside.

Father Bill Molasar: Look! Birds cover the sky!

Crowd: Ooooooooooh!

Jimbo: Dad, I'm scared! Let's get into the ark!

Father: Wait son, lets' see what else will happen. Our religious leaders told us not to go in there. If we do, everyone will think we're crazy like Noah.

Jimbo: O.K. Dad. I guess you're right.

Birds now flock from all directions, their numbers darkening the heavens, and in perfect order they go to the ark. Animals obey the command of the Great King, while people who are made in his image disobey. Guided by bright, invisible messengers, they go two and two into the ark, and the "clean" beasts by sevens.

The world looks on in wonder, some in fear.

Philosophers are called on to

Professor Flathead: This is a mystery I just can't understand. Noah is saying that messengers from the world of light are guiding these flocks of animals and birds into the ark.

No way! It's all just a coincidence! That's all I can say for it.

Camero: Boys, people have become so hardened by their persistent rejection of light that even this amazing scene has produced only a momentary impression.

Henry: I can't believe this. The flood has no danger for us three, but I tell you, if I were living among these people - I don't care what anyone said or thought - I'd run into that ark, and wouldn't come out until the flood was over!

Harry: You can say that again! After the Great King is so kind as to give the warning, and offer a way to live - and not drown to death - to reject it is insane!

Henry: It seems just as insane as what

happened to many millions of happy messengers in the Great City when they were tricked by Cosmo in the first place. It's a real mystery. I can't figure out what happens to people's brains to make them choose death instead of life.

Camero: Cosmo has given orders to his rebel army to tighten the terrible noose around the brains of the poor people. There's a supernatural power involved, and people don't know that the power of the Great King and his Prince is the only power that can help them escape from the bewitching power that Cosmo is using to control their minds. They could break away from him if they chose to follow and obey the law of the Great King, and pray to him, but they don't choose to do that. The choice is up to them. Thus, without knowing it, they end up as slaves to Cosmo - who forces their minds to greedily choose the way of death. If they die, it's their own choice and their own fault. The fiendish faggot laughs at them - knowing that one day he will see their dead bodies.

AS the doomed race beholds the sun shining in its glory and the earth clothed in almost Eden beauty, they banish their rising fears by boisterous merriment, and by their deeds of violence, seem to invite upon themselves the awful doom which is so quickly approaching.

The Great King now sends a messenger to Noah, who says, "Come with all your family into the ark; for I have seen that you are righteous before me in this wicked generation."

Camero: Boys, Noah's warnings have been rejected by the entire world, but his influence and example has resulted in saving his family. Mercy has now ceased its pleadings for the guilty race.

Harry: Oh no!

The animals and birds have now entered the place of refuge. Noah and his household are within the ark. The last call has been given. The last tear shed.

And now - - a flash of dazzling light is seen, and a cloud of glory more vivid than the lightning descends from heaven and hovers before the entrance of the ark. The massive door, which it is impossible for those within to close, is slowly swung into place by unseen hands. Noah is shut in, and the rejecters of the Great King's mercy are shut out.

Harry: What will happen now? What if someone changes his mind and decides to believe Noah's message? Can anyone get into the ark now that the door is shut?

Camero: Boys, now it's just like it was in the City when our kind and loving King was pleading with rebellious Cosmo until he became so hardened and ferocious that the announcement finally had to be made that he, and all his rebel sympathizers must leave. They had crossed over the line. The test was over, and it was shown to all that if they were given a million years more, they still wouldn't change. It was clear to the watching universe that they could not be happy there. Now, the same thing has happened to the beautiful planet which Cosmo has attacked.

Cosmo is like a virus which attacks a person and causes his cells to mutate and start a deadly cancer. Unless the cancer is gotten rid of, the mad mutation finally kills the whole body.

The seal of the Great King is upon that door. He has shut it. He alone can open it.

Henry: I feel so bad for these people outside of the ark. Look at them down there! They're more wild than I've ever seen them.

Camero: These poor doomed souls don't realize that soon, they'll be dead. They laugh, mock Noah, and party now, but very soon a great change will come over them. They don't know it, but in just a few days, everything will be different. They don't want help now, but soon - very soon, their feelings will suddenly and drastically change - only when it's too late.

For seven days after Noah and his family enter the ark, there appears no sign of the coming storm. During this time their faith is severely tested. It's a time of triumph to the world outside.

Bang, bang, bang, bang, bang.

Demitrious: Hey you morons in there! You won't show your faces ay? Stick your heads out here and we'll knock them off for you! Ha ha!

Bellini: Don't be hard on the poor fools stuck in this rat's nest!

What are ya'll varmints doin' in thar with all them animals? This is the first world zoo. Noah is the original gorilla.

Kitty: Now you guys be nice to the old man! After all, he deserves a rest after all his hard work. Thi ark is the world's first tomb. All ya have to do now is make their tomb-stone! Make it read - "Here lies old Noah, the well-meaning baboon. Hee hee.

Mophandle: Noah's three sons and their wives are in that thar hotel. They been in thar for five days now. Ain't they havin' fun! I can smell those animals now. How long ya'll gonna stay in that wooden casket? I don't think they'll ever have the nerve to come out now. They'll be too embarrassed.

Crowd: Haw haw.

Bang bang bang bang.

Kitty: Don't hit the ark too hard you guys! It might cave in! Ain't y'all glad we ain't in that zoo?

Hey you in the ark! Can ya hear me? You guys gonna croak in thar?

Mophandle, ain't ya glad you ain't one of those poor women? They sure made a mistake when they married those poor sons of Noah! Ya think they'll stay in thar till they have grandchildren?

The apparent delay confirms the masses in the belief that Noah's message is a delusion – and that the Flood will never come.

Notwithstanding the solemn scenes they've seen - - the animals and birds entering the ark, and the dazzling messenger closing the door - - they still continued their parties, even joking at these awesome manifestations of divine power.

Now great mobs gather around the ark, deriding its inmates with a daring violence they had never dared to show before.

But upon the eighth day dark clouds overspread the heavens. All of a sudden --

Boom!

A bright flash of lightning, is seen, followed by the terrific crash. From every direction is heard the distant muttering of thunder.

Henry: Look Harry, rain! Giant drops!

The laughing and shouts suddenly stop. The world has never seen anything like this. The hearts of men are struck with fear. Many now leave the ark and run for shelter from the pouring rain.

Gambezi: I don't believe this! It can't be that old Noah was right! If so, we're all doomed! Doomed, ya hear me! **Doomed!**

Demitrius: It can't be! Our scientists and

religious leaders told us that a flood is impossible! But, look at that rain! It's comin' down like it's being poured out of buckets. With all this noise, I can hardly hear what you're saying! This has never happened before! What'll we do now!

Kitty: I'm scared. **Scarrrrrred!**

Morba: Oh why didn't I get into the ark when I had a chance? What're we gonna do now? Do ya'll think Noah will open that door for us?

The jokes have stopped. All are secretly wondering - "Can it be that Noah was right, and the world is doomed to destruction?!"

Darker and darker grow the heavens, and faster comes the pounding rain.

Animals are roaming about in the wildest terror. Their crazed and frightened cries seem to moan out their own destiny, and the fate of man.

Then the fountains of the great deep are broken up, and the windows of heaven are opened. Water is seen coming from the clouds in mighty cataracts.

Rivers are braking away from their boundaries, and overflowing into the valleys. Suddenly, jets of water burst from the earth with indescribable force, throwing massive rocks hundreds of feet into the air, and these, in falling, bury themselves deep in the ground.

Rolin Rock: Oh no!!! No!!! Help me!! Aaaaahhhhh!!!

The people first see the destruction of the works of their own ands. Their splendid buildings, and the beautiful gardens and groves where they had placed their idols, are destroyed by lightning from heaven. Their ruins are blasted, and scattered far and wide. The altars on which human sacrifices have been offered are torn down. The worshipers of these dumb idols have mocked and laughed at the Great King. Now, they tremble at his power. They see that it is their own corruption which has brought their doom.

Those who a little before were so

reckless, so boastful and defiant, so exultant in their cruelty to those who have been trying to do right, are now overwhelmed with consternation and shuddering in fear. Their wails are heard above the sound of the elements. Even Cosmo and his demons acknowledge the Ruler of the universe and tremble before His power, while wicked men are supplicating for mercy and groveling in abject terror.

As the violence of the storm increases, trees, buildings, rocks, and earth are hurled in every direction. The terror of man and beast is beyond description. Above the roar of the tempest is heard the wailing of a people that have despised the authority of the King of kings.

Cosmo himself, is compelled by a great band of shining messengers - to stay down in the midst of the warring elements. He fears for his own existence.

Henry: Look! There are millions of shining messengers from the city, above Cosmo - holding him down in the horrible storm! Listen. He's yelling out something and shaking his fist.

Camero: Boys, Cosmo has delighted to control so powerful a race, and he desires them to live to practice their abominations and continue their rebellion against the Ruler of the universe. He's furious to think that they are dying.

He is now cursing the Great King and charging him with injustice and cruelty. Many of the people, like Cosmo, are blaspheming the name of the King. Many have said that they're sorry for their evil deeds - hoping to be spared. But if they were able, they would tear him from the throne of power.

Harry: Look Henry! Some of those poor wretches are frantic with fear, and are stretching their hands toward the ark and pleading for admittance.

Camero: Boys, you now hear these scoffers pleading to be let into the ark. How different their words are now than they were just the other day! How changed everything is! But their entreaties are in vain. Conscience is at last aroused to know that there is One who rules in the heavens. They're calling upon Him boys. But it's too late. In this awful hour they see that their willful transgression of the law of the universe has caused their ruin.

Harry: I hear many of them confessing their sins while they're pounding on the door of the ark. I wish they had felt like this a few days ago.

Camero: While, through fear of punishment, they acknowledge their sin Harry, they feel no true abhorrence of evil. If they were let into the ark, or if the flood was called off, they would return to their defiance of the Great King just as they were doing before the rain started.

The water rises higher and higher. The giant vessel creaks and groans as it is lifted by the surging waters. Some in their desperation now try to break into the ark, but the firm-made structure withstands their efforts. After the ark is lifted off the ground, some cling to the side of the great ship until they are carried away by the surging waters, or their hold is broken by collision with rocks and trees.

The massive ark now trembles in every fiber as it is beaten by the merciless winds and flung from billow to billow. The cries of the beasts within express their fear and pain.

Harry: We're watching all this horror, and nothing can touch us. I almost feel guilty - with all these poor people dying in the water, and here we are, safe and sound. It's like we're watching all this on T.V. - - and there's nothing we can do. Here we are in the middle of it. I wish we could do something to help them. But I know we can't. Listen to them screaming! How horrible it is to follow Cosmo and rebel against the law of the universe!

Man! This squalling wind sends chills down my back. These gigantic waves are coming at the ark like walls. If anyone ever wanted to see a perfect storm, this is it! What will happen to the ark? Will it get flipped over?

Amid the howling, blinding, warring of the elements the ark rides safely. Messengers that excel in strength are commissioned to preserve it. As the water rises higher up the mountainsides, animals rush toward man, as though expecting help from him.

Some of the people bind their children and themselves upon powerful animals, knowing that these are desperate to live, and will climb to the highest points to escape the rising waters. Some fasten themselves to towering trees. But the trees are uprooted, and with their burden of living beings are hurled into the seething billows. One spot after another that promised safety is abandoned. As the waters rise higher and higher, the people flee to the tallest mountains. Often man and beast struggle together for a foothold, until both are swept away. From the highest peaks, men look abroad upon a shoreless ocean.

Camero: Boys, the solemn warnings of

Noah no longer seem something to laugh at. How these doomed people long for the opportunities they've slighted! How they are pleading for one hour's probation, one more privilege of mercy, one more call from the lips of Noah! But the sweet voice of mercy is no more to be heard by them. Love, no less than justice, demands that the righteous judgments of the Great King should put a stop to the horrible and destructive rebellion. After one hundred and twenty years of warning against the murder and corruption, which Cosmo has inspired, to ignore it would be to approve of it.

Muldoon: Hey Mork! Can ya hear me! I'm over here! I'm up here - - in the top of this tree. I don't see anyone now but us two.

What's that? The roar is deafening. I can hardly see for this pounding rain.

Yell louder! No! I don't see anyone now but you and me! They're all dead!

Ya think we'll make it?! It looks like it's just us two in the trees on this peak!

Why in the world didn't we get into that ark!

What's that?!

No! If these waves come any higher we've had it!

Look at that would ya! There's nothin around us now but ocean. Nothing!

Hold on!

There he goes.

Mork: Aaaaaaaaaaaaaaaaaaaaaahhhhhhhhh!!!

The avenging waters sweep over the last retreat, and the despisers of the Great King and his law of love perish in the black depths.

Camero: Boys, they're gone. It's hard to believe that a whole planet of people are gone! Only eight people are left in the entire world. And they're in the ark. But it was their choice. The Great Prince has said, "All they that hate me love death." They all said they wanted life, and they screamed and yelled for it. But they chose death, and their desire was granted.

Harry: At least it's a relief to me that their suffering is over. I've heard that a human loses consciousness under water in 90 seconds. Is that true?

Camero: That's approximately right.

Harry: I'm glad they didn't suffer longer - even if they deserved it. Is that all the punishment the wicked people will get? And what about the good people who were murdered by the evil ones? Some of them suffered in death more that the wicked suffered in the water. How can I look at the whole thing of death as being fair?

Camero: The answer is because both good and evil people die the first time, but that's not their final reward.

Harry: You mean there's more?

Camero: Much more.

Henry: If good and evil people don't get their final reward in this life, how and when do they get it?

Camero: The ones who were faithful and obedient to the law of the Great King, and who trusted in the great deliverance provided by him through the gift of the death of his Son in your place - - they will get their great reward when the Son of the King comes to earth the second time.

The first time he comes as a poor and helpless baby, he will be put to death by the very world he came to save. Then, when his Father calls him, he will raise himself from the dead, and go back to his Father. He will have power to lay his life down in your place, and he will have power to take it up again.

Harry: Wow! Whoever heard of someone having power to raise himself from the dead!

Camero: You can see that our Great Prince is more than human. He has the same power to uphold the vast universe that his Father does. Both of them together uphold it. Together, they made it. And you got a little glimpse of how vast it is when you were going through it - when you felt like fainting.

Henry: I remember!

Camero: After a time, the Great Prince will come back to earth the second time - appearing in the sky with power and great brightness so that every eye on earth will see him. Then, he will take those who have loved and obeyed him up through space in a gigantic caravan to the Great City.

Harry: Is that when the goal of the Great King will be fulfilled - when earth people sit on thrones with him - co-ruling the universe?

Camero: That's right Harry. That will be a happy day for the entire universe! Cosmo will try to stop it from happening. But he can't.

While we were still in the city, you asked how a person could get to live there. Now you know.

Henry: That's right! I understand it better now than if you'd tried to tell me before the world was made, and before I'd seen all the horrors that Cosmo has been bringing on the people.

Camero: As the time of their probation was closing, the people who are now dead and floating in the water, gave themselves up to exciting parties and festivities. Those who had influence and power were bent on keeping the minds of the masses engrossed with pleasure and excitement lest any should be impressed by the last solemn warning.

I'm going to tell you something now. Down in the twenty first century - where you came from, the same thing is going to happen just before the King's Son comes to the earth the second time to deliver his people from again being murdered by the wicked.

In other words, like it has been now in Noah's day - when the wicked were destroyed by water, it will be again in your day - about 4000 years from now - when the wicked will be destroyed by fire.

Harry: Destroyed by fire? What does that mean?

Camero: You're going to see the answer to that with your own eyes Harry. But keep in mind that the original plan of the Great King will be fulfilled. Nothing can stop that from happening. Down in your day, the people will be much the same as the ones we've been watching for the past few years - as they've been mocking Noah. There will be many parallels. As the scientists have said that all the people couldn't be destroyed by water, scientists will again say that they cannot be destroyed by fire. And as the world mocked Noah and his family for giving the warning of love in this day, the wicked will again mock obedient and loving people for giving the world the last warning then.

So the answer to your question about the reward of the good and evil is answered in the fact that the people will get their real reward for their deeds not in this life, but after they are judged, and get to either live with the Great King and Prince in joy forever, or receive the second and final death that Cosmo will receive when he and his fellow rebels are turned to ashes.

Henry: Wow!

The waters rise fifteen cubits above the highest mountains. Amid the dark and howling tempest, it often seems to the little family that they must perish as for five long months the ark is tossed at the mercy of howling wind and wave. It's a trying ordeal, but Noah's faith in the love and promises of the Great King doesn't waver. He has the assurance that the divine hand is on the helm.

Camero: Boys, you notice that as the waters are beginning to go down, our good King is causing the ark to drift into this spot protected by a group of mountains which have been preserved by his power. These mountains are like a nest of peaks, only a little distance apart. The ark now moves about in this quiet haven, and is no longer driven and beaten upon the boundless ocean. This is giving great relief to the weary, tempest-tossed voyagers.

Henry: It's kind of him to do that.

Noah and his family anxiously wait for the decrease of the waters, for they long to get out of the ark and get back on solid ground again. Forty days after the tops of the mountains are seen, they send out a raven - a bird of quick scent, to discover whether the earth has become dry. This bird, finding nothing but water, and slippery, rocky peaks, continues to fly to and from the ark. Seven days later a dove is sent out. She finds no real footing either, and returns to the ark. Noah waits another week and gain sends out the dove. When she returns at evening with an olive leaf in her mouth, the sound of great rejoicing comes from the exhausted travelers inside. Later Noah removes the covering of the ark, and looks around.

Noah: Oh my children! Look!

Shem: What is it Dad?

Noah: Land! Most of the ground is dry!

Family: Hurraah! Woopie!

Japheth: Finally! We can go out on the ground again.

Ham: That'll be great!

Still Noah waits patiently within the ark. As he had entered at the command of the Great King, he waits for special directions to depart.

Cosmo: Listen to those triangleheads in the ark! The Great King is hoping that now he can start all over again, and fill the earth with people who will love and obey him. He wants a whole planet full of people who are kind, unselfish, and loving - just like himself! Ha!

I'll show him two things or three. Listen now you boneheads. We'll corrupt the earth worse than it was before! We took control of those stooges whose bodies are floating in the water. We tricked them into mating with animals to produce those weird cave people. One day, the whole world would have been filled with half man, half animal until it finally became mostly animal and just enough man to obey me forever! But this pesky flood ruined my plans. Someday, I'll do it again. If he wants the world to be pure, he's going to be disappointed! We'll never let him succeed. He wants to show the other planets that he can have a world with people like Himself and his Prince. I'll show the universe that no one can obey any law except the great law of Cosmo! Hey hey!

He says that his law is the law of unselfishness where people love each other and live to make others happy. Ha! I'll make the world slaves to my law of selfishness so that they'll live to make no one happy but themselves.

"Number one!" That's my motto.

"I, I, I, myself, I.
The what and the where, the how and the why.
the big and the small, the low and the high.
I, I, I, myself I."

After these eight goons come out of the ark, we'll make their descendants so full of self, so greedy, and such lovers of pleasure, that the Great City would be a bore. If they ever got there, they'd rob the place blind. They'd set up gambling casinos, and turn it into a circus, a red light district, and a battlefield until everyone was dead.

Kliptoria: Maybe that's why we ain't there.

Cosmo: I was just dreaming you molehead. Such a thing can't happen in the great city. But we're going to make it happen on planet earth! Hey hey!

Slipto: If we get the new world following us like the old world did, will they all be happy?

Cosmo: Are you kidding! The cricketheads who follow my law of self will be so miserable that many of them will kill themselves! Hey hey!

Morgonia: I thought you told us that if we follow you, you'll make us happier than we were with the Great King, and his law.

Cosmo: Haven't you learned by now that all I give you is a pack of lies?

Miptoria: Yea, we learned that when we found ourselves with you in hell - in the blackness of outer space! But I'm surprised that you're confessing this to us.

Cosmo: I only tell you because you're my slaves and there's nothing you can do about it. Hey hey! You might as well sing and swing and celebrate. You've got my nature, and now you think like I do. We're in this together, and you will work with me against the Great King. That's all the fun you're going to get boys.

Zelmona: We know! You can't fool us

352

any more. We know we're going to die like these miserable people whose bodies are floating in the water.

Cosmo: I don't want to hear about our death you toad head. We've got a lot of work to do. Try to take pleasure in fighting against the Great King and his Prince. Work to bring on the ruin of these humans - for that's what we're living for now. That's the only joy you weed heads are ever going to get. We must drag them down lower than the animals so that when the Great Prince invades our territory and comes to earth in human form, the brains of the people will be so dull that they won't see his love for them. We must make the earthlings think that the Great Prince is selfish like us! When he comes to earth, we must get the humans to reject his love and his law of love. When he comes to earth, we must get them to murder him. We must beat him at his own game! We must win! We've got to win! Death to the humans!

Rebel army: Death to the humans!

Cosmo: Death to planet earth!

Rebel army: Death to planet earth!

Cosmo: Death to the Great Prince!

Rebel army: Death to the Great Prince!

Cosmo: If we have to die, we're going to take the earthlings with us! We'll start with these puppet heads in the ark. Hey hey!

What horrors are in store for the little family as they come out of the ark?

What will happen with Cosmo's devilish plan for the coming "Battle of Armageddon" as earth races through space into the 21st century?

Get the amazing follow-up book, *Patriarchs and Prophets*. You'll be boggled. You may call toll free {1-877-439-4800} for a quick credit card order, or you may use the handy order form on the next page. Shipping is included, and you'll also receive the "NSL" bonus book - answering many questions about Cosmo's tricks in our day, and showing one of his most shocking attacks against us now!

Also, on the next page, you may order more of this book *Cousin Henry Potter {and the Terrible Time Machine}* to give as gifts to those you know and love!